Mammals of
Madagascar

Lynx Illustrated Checklist of the
Mammals of Madagascar
with the Comoros, the Seychelles, Réunion and Mauritius

AUTHORS
Russell A. Mittermeier
Olivier M. Langrand
Don E. Wilson
Anthony B. Rylands
Jonah H. Ratsimbazafy
Kim E. Reuter
Tina Andriamanana
Edward E. Louis Jr.
Christoph Schwitzer
Wes Sechrest

CONTRIBUTORS
Voahangy Soarimalala
Steven M. Goodman
Paula D. Jenkins
Connor J. Burgin
Thomas E. Lacher Jr.
Rene de Roland Lily Arison
Serge Rajaobelina
Patricia C. Wright

MARGOT MARSH
BIODIVERSITY
FOUNDATION

First Edition: May 2021

© Lynx Edicions – Montseny, 8, 08193 Bellaterra, Barcelona, www.lynxeds.com

Based on texts of the *Handbook of the Mammals of the World* (HMW) series, with modifications and updates. Compiled by Andrew Elliott.

Illustrations by Toni Llobet, Faansie Peacock, Ilian Velikov, Jesús Rodríguez-Osorio, Lluís Sogorb, Francesc Jutglar, Àlex Mascarell and Stephen D. Nash.

Project co-ordinator: Amy Chernasky
Map production: Anna Motis
Layout and interior book design: Elena Fonts Circuns

Cover illustration by Ilian Velikov
Indri (*Indri indri*)

Printed and bound in Barcelona by Índice Arts Gràfiques.
Legal Deposit: B 5551-2021
ISBN: 978-84-16728-48-0

This book is dedicated to Doris and Dale Swanson of Spokane, Washington, USA, in recognition of their many generous contributions to species conservation, and especially for their critical early support to the *Handbook of the Mammals of the World* series.

AUTHORS

Russell A. Mittermeier
Chief Conservation Officer, Re:wild, Austin, Texas, USA; and Chair, IUCN SSC Primate Specialist Group.

Olivier M. Langrand
Executive Director, Critical Ecosystem Partnership Fund (CEPF), Arlington, Virginia, USA.

Don E. Wilson
Curator Emeritus, National Museum of Natural History, Washington DC, USA.

Anthony B. Rylands
Primate Conservation Director, Re:wild, Austin, Texas, USA; and Deputy Chair, IUCN SSC Primate Specialist Group.

Jonah H. Ratsimbazafy
President, GERP (Groupe d'Étude et de Recherche sur les Primates de Madagascar), Antananarivo, Madagascar; and Vice Chair, IUCN SSC Primate Specialist Group.

Kim E. Reuter
Board Member, Lemur Love, San Diego, California, USA; and Deputy Chair, IUCN SSC Primate Specialist Group.

Tina Andriamanana
Executive Director, Fanamby, Antananarivo, Madagascar.

Edward E. Louis Jr.
Director, Conservation Genetics Department, Omaha's Henry Doorly Zoo and Aquarium, Nebraska, USA; and Director General, Madagascar Biodiversity Partnership, Antananarivo, Madagascar.

Christoph Schwitzer
Director, Dublin Zoo, Dublin, Ireland; and Deputy Chair, IUCN SSC Primate Specialist Group.

Wes Sechrest
Chief Scientist and CEO, Re:wild, Austin, Texas, USA.

CONTRIBUTORS

Voahangy Soarimalala
Senior Researcher, Association Vahatra, Antananarivo; and Professor, Institut des Sciences et Techniques de l'Environnement, Université de Fianarantsoa, Fianarantsoa, Madagascar.

Steven M. Goodman
MacArthur Field Biologist, Field Museum of Natural History, Chicago, Illinois, USA.

Paula D. Jenkins
Senior Curator, Mammal Collection, Department of Life Sciences, The Natural History Museum, London, UK.

Connor J. Burgin
PhD Student, Department of Biology, University of New Mexico, Albuquerque, New Mexico, USA.

Thomas E. Lacher Jr.
Professor, Department of Ecology and Conservation Biology, Texas A&M University, College Station; and Senior Associate Conservation Scientist, Re:wild, Austin, Texas, USA.

Rene de Roland Lily Arison
National Director, The Peregrine Fund Madagascar Project, Antananarivo, Madagascar.

Serge Rajaobelina
Founder, Fanamby, Antananarivo, Madagascar.

Patricia C. Wright
Herrnstein Chair in Conservation Biology, Stony Brook University, Stony Brook, New York, USA; and Founder and International Director, Centre ValBio Research Campus, Ranomafana, Madagascar.

Contents

Introduction

We are very pleased to present the latest and most comprehensive guide to the *Mammals of Madagascar*. It is based on Lynx Edicions' recent *Illustrated Checklist of the Mammals of the World* (Burgin *et al.*, 2020), which included updates on the lemur fauna as presented in *Lemurs of Madagascar* (Mittermeier *et al.*, 2010) and its subsequent French edition, *Les Lémuriens de Madagascar* (Mittermeier *et al.*, 2014), as well as the latest information on other Malagasy mammal groups (Albignac, 1973; Garbutt, 1999, 2007; Goodman, 2011, 2012; Soarimalala & Goodman, 2011).

Madagascar is truly a very special country. It is without a doubt one of the highest-priority Biodiversity Hotspots on our planet (Mittermeier *et al.*, 1999, 2004; Mittermeier & Rylands, 2017), besides being a top-priority Megadiversity Country (Mittermeier *et al.*, 1997). It is also the world's fourth largest island, and the largest oceanic island. Following the fracture of the eastern part of the Gondwana supercontinent about 160 million years ago (South America was the western part) and the island's subsequent separation from what is now the Indian Subcontinent around 90 million years ago, Madagascar's flora and fauna have evolved largely in isolation. The result is that the country has very high levels of endemism at the species, genus and family levels. Indeed, at the time of publication, we recognize no less than 22 families of plants and vertebrate animals that are endemic to this island country, and three others that are near-endemic (each with a single species reaching the nearby Comoros).

The diversity of plants in Madagascar is extraordinary, with a total of 11,698 species of vascular plants in 1,698 genera currently recognized. An additional 950 forms are candidate species, and, based on ongoing and future taxonomic research, it is estimated that the documented flora of Madagascar will eventually amount to at least 14,000 species. By comparison, continental Africa has about 77,000 species over an area that is 52 times larger than Madagascar (Lowry *et al.*, 2018). Five plant families are strictly endemic to Madagascar: Asteropeiaceae, eight species of trees and shrubs in a single genus; Barbeuiaceae, a single species of liana; Physenaceae, with two species in one genus of small trees and shrubs; Sarcolaenaceae, with 72 species in 10 genera, including evergreen trees and shrubs; and Sphaerosepalaceae, 14 species in two genera of deciduous trees.

For freshwater fish, there are 122 endemic species recognized from Madagascar. They include two endemic families: Bedotiidae, the Malagasy rainbowfish, with two genera; and Anchariidae, the Malagasy catfishes, also with two genera. The number of endemic freshwater fish species known on the island is certain to increase because many small river basins and watersheds have yet to be thoroughly inventoried.

The native amphibians of Madagascar are all endemic, with 341 known species and an additional 200 possible species still being studied (Vences & Raselimanana, 2018). There is one endemic family, Mantellidae, which consists of 12 genera, the best known of which are the brightly coloured members of the genus *Mantella*. There are also three endemic subfamilies of narrow-mouthed frogs in the family Microhylidae: Cophylinae (74 species in eight genera); Scaphiophryninae (11 species in two genera); and Dyscophinae (three species in a single genus, the famed tomato frogs). There is also an endemic genus of African sedge or bush frogs in the family Hyperoliidae (Malagasy reed frogs), with 11 species.

Reptiles are represented by 417 species, 98% of which are endemic, including two endemic families and one near-endemic: Opluridae, the Malagasy iguanas, with eight species in two genera (just one species shared with the Comoros); Sanziniidae, with four species of booid snakes in two genera; and the monotypic Xenotyphlopidae, the Round-nosed Blind Snake (Glaw & Raselimanana, 2018). There are no endemic families of turtles and tortoises, but there are three noteworthy endemic genera: *Asterochelys*, with two species, the Radiated Tortoise *Asterochelys radiata* and the nearly extinct Ploughshare Tortoise or Angonoka *Asterochelys yniphora*; *Pyxis*, with two species and four taxa of small tortoises; and *Erymnochelys*, large freshwater turtles whose closest living relatives are found in northern South America.

Turning to the birds, there are 110 endemic species, with four endemic and two near-endemic families; the mesites, Mesitornithidae, with three terrestrial species in two genera; the ground rollers, Brachypteraciidae, with five species in four genera; the Madagascar Cuckoo-Roller of the monotypic family Leptosomidae (also found in the Comoros); the false sunbirds or asities,

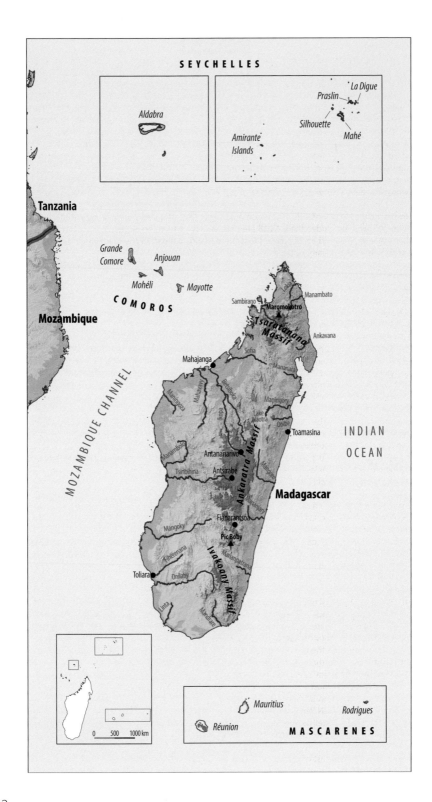

SEYCHELLES

Aldabra

Praslin

La Digue

Silhouette

Mahé

Amirante
Islands

Tanzania

Grande
Comore

Anjouan

Mohéli

Mayotte

COMOROS

Sambirano

Manambato

Maromokotro

Tsaratanana
Massif

Ankavana

Mozambique

Sofia

Mananara

Mahajanga

Mahavavy

Betsiboka

Maningory

Lake
Alaotra

Onibe

Toamasina

INDIAN
OCEAN

Mangoro

Antananarivo

Antsirabe

Ankaratra Massif

Madagascar

MOZAMBIQUE CHANNEL

Manambolo

Tsiribihina

Mangoky

Fianarantsoa

Pic Boby

Mananpatrana

Ivakoany Massif

Tihereriana

Toliara

Onilahy

Linta

Mandrare

0   500   1000 km

Mauritius

Réunion

Rodrigues

MASCARENES

Philepittidae, with four species in two genera; the Malagasy warblers, Bernieridae, an ancient clade (at least nine million years old) with 11 species in eight genera; and last, the shrike-like vangas, Vangidae, with 20 species in 14 genera (one species in the Comoros [Safford & Hawkins, 2013; Sinclair & Langrand, 2013]).

Finally, we come to to the mammals, the subject of this guide. There are eight endemic families (Tenrecidae, Cheirogaleidae, Lepilemuridae, Lemuridae, Indriidae, Daubentoniidae, Myzopodidae and Eupleridae), and 40 endemic genera (eight of insectivores, nine of rodents, one of bats, seven of carnivores, and 15 of lemurs), truly amazing numbers for a country the size of Madagascar. Of the 219 native terrestrial species, 212 (96.8%) are endemic—31 insectivores (all endemic), 28 rodents (all endemic), 45 bats (37 of them endemic, one near-endemic), seven carnivores (all endemic), and 108 lemurs (all endemic). In addition, 34 marine species, none of them endemic, have been recorded in the waters surrounding Madagascar.

On the neighbouring islands of the Comoros, Seychelles and Mascarenes, a total of 18 native mammals have been identified. All 18 are bats, and 13 of them are endemic to one or more of these islands. It should also be noted that these islands are part of the Madagascar and Indian Ocean Islands Biodiversity Hotspot (Mittermeier *et al.*, 2004).

The family Tenrecidae is made up of three subfamilies: Tenrecine, five species of small hedgehog-like mammals in four genera, *Tenrec*, *Setifer*, *Echinops* and *Hemicentetes*; Geogalinae, a small, shrew-like termite-eater, the Large-eared Tenrec *Geogale aurita*; and Oryzorictinae, with three genera, two rice tenrecs in the genus *Oryzorictes,* and 23 shrew tenrecs in the genera *Nesogale* and *Microgale* (Goodman, Soarimalala & Olson, 2018).

Notable too is an endemic subfamily of rodents, Nesomyinae (family Nesomyidae), composed of 28 rats and mice in nine genera—*Brachytarsomys* (two tree rats with small feet), *Gymnuromys* (a ground rat), *Voalavo* (two forest mice), *Eliurus* (13 rats with tufted tails), *Macrotarsomys* (three rats with large feet), *Monticolomys* (a montane forest mouse), *Hypogeomys* (the Giant Jumping Rat), *Brachyuromys* (two mice with short tails) and *Nesomys* (three forest rats) (Goodman & Soarimalala, 2018).

Our knowledge of the bat fauna of Madagascar has increased significantly in the past 15 years. Of the 45 bat species found on the island, 38 (84.5%) are endemic or near-endemic (a single species also found in the Comoros), with seven (15.5%) also found in Africa. The endemic family Myzopodidae comprises two sucker-footed bats in the genus *Myzopoda*; these have small sucker-like cups on their wrists and ankles, which they use to secure themselves to the undersides of the large leaves where they roost (Goodman & Ramasindrazana, 2018).

The family Eupleridae is a small but remarkable radiation of carnivores, with seven distinct genera, six of them monotypic. *Cryptoprocta* is the genus of the Fosa, the largest of the Malagasy carnivores, as agile in the trees as it is on the ground; it is a predator of birds and mammals, including lemurs. Of the other genera, the very unusual Falanouc (*Eupleres*) eats worms, snails and other small invertebrates, as do the smaller, similarly mongoose-like vontsiras (*Galidia*, *Galidictis* and *Salanoia*), and the even more diminutive Bokyboky (*Mungotictis*). The other genus is the Spotted Fanaloka (*Fossa*).

The endemic terrestrial non-primate mammals have experienced significant human-induced extinctions in the past couple of thousand years. Amongst those that have already disappeared are: two species of Malagasy aardvark (*Plesiorycteropus germainepetterae* and *P. madagascariensis*); one species of tenrec (*Microgale macpheei*); two bats (*Hipposideros besaoka* and *Triaenops goodmani*); one carnivore, the Giant Fosa (*Cryptoprocta spelea*), estimated to have been the size of a Grey Wolf *Canis lupus*; three species of hippopotamus (*Hippopotamus guldbergi*, *H. laloumena* and *H. lemerli*); and three rodents in the endemic subfamily Nesomyinae (*Brachytarsomys mahajambaensis*, *Hypogeomys australis* and *Nesomys narindaensis*). On top of these extinctions, the threat level to the extant non-primate mammal species is also relatively high, with 25 (22%) of them threatened (in the IUCN Red List categories of Endangered and Vulnerable). The aforementioned extinct mammals, as well as the extinct lemurs mentioned below, are described and beautifully illustrated in the book *Extinct Madagascar: Picturing the Island's Past* (Goodman and Jungers, 2014).

Notwithstanding this list of extraordinary endemic species that characterize the flora and fauna of Madagascar, the country's uniqueness is best exemplified by its non-human primates, the lemurs. Madagascar has a total of 108 species of lemur, two of which have three subspecies, making for an overall total of 112 lemur taxa, and constituting an unparalleled primate radiation that is wholly endemic to this island (two species were introduced to the Comoro Islands, and are now established there). This number of species places Madagascar second only to Brazil, the world leader in primate diversity. This is all the more remarkable when one realizes that Madagascar—at 587,040 km^2, a little larger than France, about 20% smaller than Texas and 28% larger than the state of California in the USA—is only 7% the size of Brazil. Madagascar's lemur fauna is even more impressive when one considers the higher taxonomic levels—five families and 15 genera of living lemurs, again all of them endemic. Compare this once more to Brazil, with 130 primate species and 151 taxa, respectively 88 and 58% of which are endemic, but just five of Brazil's 22 genera are endemic, and none of its five primate families.

Looking at Madagascar's primate diversity in another way, although it is only one of 91 countries that have wild primate populations, it alone is home to 16% of all primate species and subspecies (112 out of 706), 19% of all primate genera (15/80), and 31% of all primate families (5/16, all five of them endemic). Clearly, if we lose the lemur fauna of Madagascar, it will have a major impact on primate diversity worldwide.

Analysing Madagascar's primate diversity in yet another way, small though the island is in a global context, we consider it to be one of the world's four major regions for primates. Indeed, its 15 genera and 112 taxa are comparable to the entire Neotropical region (22 genera and 216 taxa), all of mainland Africa and associated islands (27 genera and 192 taxa), and all of tropical, subtropical and temperate Asia (19 genera and 187 taxa), in spite of occupying just 0.4% of the Earth's land area.

Furthermore, the lemur fauna of Madagascar is the world's single highest primate conservation priority, with fully 105 species and subspecies (94%) considered threatened, based on the most recent assessments carried out by the IUCN Species Survival Commission's Primate Specialist Group for the IUCN Red List of Threatened Species (2020). This puts lemurs among the world's most threatened larger groups of mammals, and indeed among the most-threatened groups of vertebrates overall. Thirty-four percent of the lemur taxa are considered Critically Endangered (38/112), 40% Endangered (44/112), and 21% Vulnerable (23/112), with some of the Critically Endangered down to extremely low population levels. Indeed, without proper measures, we could be facing a major primate extinction episode in the very near future.

Madagascar also clearly demonstrates that recent primate and other mammal extinctions, as indicated above, are a real phenomenon, and not just a figment of the conservationist's fertile imagination. Fully eight genera and at least 17 species of lemur have already gone extinct on the island since the arrival of our own species roughly 2,500 years ago—although there is some evidence that early human migrants might have been present as long as 10,000 years ago (Anderson *et al.*, 2018; Mitchell, 2020; Wright & Rakotoarisoa, in press). All of the lemurs that are known to have disappeared, some as recently as about 500 years ago, were larger than existing species. The family Archaeolemuridae included two genera and three species. *Archaeolemur edwardsi* and *A. majori* were stocky (15–25 kg) and evidently terrestrial, and comparable to baboons or macaques. They are referred to as the "monkey lemurs", and were widespread in Madagascar till AD 1047–1280. The second genus in this family had only one species, *Hadropithecus stenognathus*, rather larger at 27–35 kg and also terrestrial. It is believed to have gone extinct earlier, around AD 444–472.

More is known about the family Palaeopropithecidae, referred to as the "sloth-lemurs", with eight species identified in four genera. Three species in the genus *Palaeopropithecus*—*P. ingens*, *P. maximus* and *P. kelyus*—are considered the most specialized, with a body mass range of 35–50 kg. They were adapted for arboreal suspensory locomotion, rather like the living Neotropical sloths, but much larger. They were evidently widespread through Madagascar, and fossils have been dated to 680 to 510 years ago; they may have survived until AD 1300–1620. *Archaeoindris fontoynontii*, known from just one fossil site, was very much larger, reaching 200 kg—the size of a male gorilla— and is thought to have been similar to the giant ground sloths of Pleistocene South America. Astonishingly, it is believed to have occupied the high plateau areas of Madagascar until as recently as 350 BC. The smaller *Babakotia radofilai* (10–14 kg) had long forelimbs, and strong, grasping hands and feet, and was probably the most similar to the South American sloths. The fourth genus in the family, *Mesopropithecus*, had three species currently known of—*M. dolichobrachion*, *M. globiceps* and *M. pithecoides*. They also weighed 10–14 kg, and had heads resembling those of sifakas but the forelimbs (not the hindlimbs, as in the leaping sifakas) somewhat elongated,

Mesopropithecus

Indri

Pachylemur

Babakotia

Megaladapis

Palaeopropithecus

Hadropithecus

Archaeoindris

0   50
cm

Archaeolemur

Reconstructions of the eight subfossil lemur genera already extinct in Madagascar. The Indri, the largest of the living genera, is included in silhouette to show scale. Artwork by Stephen D. Nash, based on information provided by L. R. Godfrey and W. L. Jungers.

indicating suspensory locomotion, although they were probably more quadrupedal than the other species in this family.

The family Megaladapidae is known from three species in a single genus, *Megaladapis*—*M. grandidieri*, *M. edwardsi* and *M. madagascariensis*. They are called the "koala lemurs" because of their short arms and legs, but they were considerably larger than the modern Australian Koala *Phascolarctos cinereus*, which, of course, is unrelated. They weighed around 45–85 kg, and from their dentition it is possible to infer that they were folivores; a shelf of bone above the nose indicates that they had a mobile snout. It is believed that they lived until at least AD 1280–1420.

In addition to these extinct families, there are two species of *Pachylemur*, an extinct genus of the still extant Lemuridae. *P. insignis* and *P. jullyi* were found in central and south-western Madagascar, and they weighed about 10–13 kg, a little larger than the largest of the living lemurs. Their crania were similar to those of the ruffed lemurs, *Varecia*, but they had a more robust skeleton. Long-tailed, arboreal frugivores, they are thought to have lived until AD 1280–1420.

The last known subfossil is a giant Aye-aye, *Daubentonia robusta*, of the still extant family Daubentoniidae. It has been estimated to have weighed about 14 kg, much larger than the 3-kg living species of aye-aye. An arboreal quadruped with a limited capacity to leap, it is known to have survived at least until AD 891–1027.

If we count these eight recently extinct genera together with the 15 extant genera, we come to a total of 23 primate genera that were found on Madagascar until just a few hundred to a few thousand years ago, a truly remarkable number that exceeds the number of genera in all of the Neotropics and in all of Asia, being only slightly behind Africa! As already noted, many other lemurs could join the extinct list within the next few decades if rapid and large-scale action is not taken.

Marine mammals are also well represented around Madagascar, with a total of 34 species encountered in the Madagascar Exclusive Economic Zone (EEZ). However, there is very little information on almost all of these species, their ecology, their movements, and their migration patterns in Malagasy waters. One exception is the Humpback Whale *Megaptera novaeangliae*. This species continues to recover from the impact of commercial whaling that took place in the past two centuries. Baie d'Antongil and Île Sainte Marie in the north-east of Madagascar are important mating sites for this species, and it is estimated that some 7,000 individuals meet in this breeding aggregation area.

Regrettably, threats to the natural environment in Madagascar have been increasing hugely in recent decades. The threats to lemurs, other mammals, and indeed all of Madagascar's biodiversity include widespread deforestation due to slash-and-burn agriculture (called *tavy* in Madagascar), logging (legal and illegal), mining, charcoal production, fuelwood collection, seasonal burning of grasslands to create a "green bite" for cattle (which often ignites nearby forest patches), and live capture of lemurs for pets. Recent severe desertification in the southern part of the country has resulted in human migrations northward to areas of forest, often within protected areas. Sadly, the hunting of lemurs as a source of food, a threat previously thought to be less severe than for primates in other parts of the world, has emerged over the past couple of decades as another major problem in Madagascar, and requires special attention.

Given the amazing diversity of Madagascar's flora and fauna and its enormous global importance, it is very sobering to reflect on the extent of the degradation and loss of its forest habitat. By the 1950s, only 27% of Madagascar was still forested (down from approximately 90% when humans first arrived [Humbert & Cours Darne, 1965]), and by 2005 this percentage had dropped to an estimated 17% (Harper *et al.*, 2007; MEFT, USAID & CI, 2009). About 500 km² of forest were lost each year from 2000 to 2009, and it is highly likely that more than that has disappeared annually in the ensuing decade. We estimate that no more than 10% of Madagascar's natural vegetation remains, an area that would be equivalent to about three times the small state of New Jersey in the USA, about the size of Sri Lanka, or about three-quarters the size of Ireland. This is an extremely small area to ensure the survival of one of the most important and distinctive collections of life on Earth.

As if this were not serious enough, it should be remembered that fragmentation and isolation of forest fragments is also extreme. Harper *et al.* (2007) calculated that the area of what they called

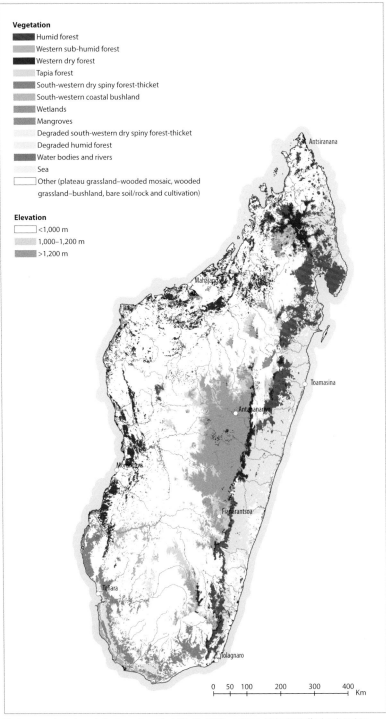

Madagascar: principal vegetation types. From Moat & Smith (2007), version published in Safford and Hawkins (2013), reproduced here with the permission of Bloomsbury Publishing, London.

Vegetation
- Humid forest
- Western sub-humid forest
- Western dry forest
- Tapia forest
- South-western dry spiny forest-thicket
- South-western coastal bushland
- Wetlands
- Mangroves
- Degraded south-western dry spiny forest-thicket
- Degraded humid forest
- Water bodies and rivers
- Sea
- Other (plateau grassland–wooded mosaic, wooded grassland–bushland, bare soil/rock and cultivation)

Elevation
- <1,000 m
- 1,000–1,200 m
- >1,200 m

17

"core forest" (forest more than 1 km from a forest edge) decreased from more than 90,000 km^2 in the 1950s to less than 20,000 km^2 in 2000, and that the area in patches of 100 km^2 or more decreased by more than half in that period. Of the forest that remained in 1973, a further 37% was lost by 2014, with an annual deforestation rate of 1.1%/year from 2010 to 2014. Almost half (46%) of Madagascar's surviving forest is now located less than 100 m from the forest edge (Vieilledent et al., 2018).

The conservation of Madagascar's exceptional biodiversity requires an ambitious and comprehensive network of protected areas. The first ten natural reserves were created as early as 1927, during the French colonial period. More protected areas were gazetted following Madagascar's independence in 1960, and in the late 1980s there was an upsurge in the creation of protected areas. With the support of international conservation organizations such as the World Wide Fund for Nature (WWF) and Conservation International (CI), as well as the World Bank, the US Agency for International Development, the Global Environment Facility (GEF), and the German Development Bank (KfW), the government of Madagascar developed administrative structures to manage biodiversity and increase the legal coverage of protected areas. Nevertheless, by 2003 only about 3% of Madagascar's land area was protected, corresponding to around 17,000 km^2, and only a small portion of this was effectively managed.

The most important and dramatic change took place in September 2003, when, during the IUCN World Parks Congress in Durban, South Africa, Madagascar's then president announced his commitment to triple the protected area coverage. As part of this, he requested that the international community come up with a fund of $50 million to make it possible. International conservation organizations and bilateral and multilateral governmental entities stepped up, which resulted in the creation in 2005 of the Fondation pour les Aires Protégées et la Biodiversité de Madagascar (FAPBM), also known as the Madagascar Biodiversity Fund, still in existence and now capitalized at about $70 million.

In 2008, an analysis of gaps in the conservation of Madagascar's terrestrial ecosystems was carried out by national and international experts. It resulted in the creation of new protected areas covering 43,260 km^2, dramatically increasing the area covered by the existing Madagascar national parks sites that previously totalled 26,380 km^2.

The network of protected areas has continued to evolve over the past decade. Altogether 122 officially decreed protected areas, covering 71,777.6 km^2, are now recognized (Goodman, Raherilalao & Wohlhauser, 2018). As a result, 12% of Madagascar is now legally protected and managed by the government, by national and international non-governmental organizations operating in Madagascar, and by local community associations.

Today, the government of Madagascar is managing 43 protected areas through a parastatal organization called Madagascar National Parks (MNP), with core funding provided by the above-mentioned FAPBM and various international donors. These protected areas belong to IUCN Categories I, II and IV.

In contrast, protected areas of IUCN Categories III, V and VI are managed by local, national and international non-governmental organizations. National NGOs, in particular, play a key role in the management of protected areas, including Asity (4 sites); Fanamby (5); Association Tahosoa Alandriake Mitambatse (TAMIA) (1); Association Vondrona Ivon'ny Fampandrosoana (VIF) (1); Biodiversity Conservation Madagascar (BCM) (2); Département de Biologie et Ecologie Végétale (DBEV) (1); Development and Environmental Law Center Madagascar (DELC) (1); Ecole Supérieure des Sciences Agronomiques – Forêts (ESSA-Forêts) (1); Fikambanana Bongolava Maitso (FBM) (1); Groupe d'Etude et de Recherche sur les Primates de Madagascar (GERP) (1); Madagasikara Voakajy (7); Sauvegarde de l'Environnement et pour le Développement Intégré de Madagascar (SEDIM) (1); and Service d'Appui à la Gestion de l'Environnement (SAGE) (1).

International NGOs have also been involved in the management of protected areas for four decades, and this engagement continues with Conservation International (3), Durrell Wildlife Conservation Trust (3), Missouri Botanical Garden (MBG) (12), Muséum national d'Histoire naturelle (MNHN) (1), The Peregrine Fund (4), QIT Madagascar Minerals (QMM) (3), Royal Botanic Gardens, Kew (1), Wildlife Conservation Society (WCS) (5), and the World Wide Fund for Nature (WWF) (5) (Rakotoson & Razafimahatratra, 2018).

In addition to these protected areas, there are those protected under the Ramsar Convention. This convention, dedicated to the conservation of wetlands of global importance, was ratified by Madagascar in 1998. Subsequently, Madagascar proposed a number of lakes, swamps, rivers and estuaries to be considered as Ramsar sites, to the point that 21 have now been designated. They provide protection to some unique wetland ecosystems and cover 21,480 km^2.

Significant progress has been made in the past 20 years to conserve the terrestrial biodiversity of Madagascar, but little effort has been dedicated to the conservation of marine biodiversity. Madagascar is lagging behind in the creation of Marine Protected Areas (MPA), with less than 1% of its Exclusive Economic Zone (EEZ) of 1,200,000 km^2 currently legally protected. The 17 existing MPAs are in many cases an extension of existing terrestrial protected areas, and they tend to be small, focusing on specific habitats, and with an absence of a strategic seascape design. For the most part, the emphasis has been put on coastal biodiversity conservation, in particular through the promotion of Locally Managed Marine Protected Areas (LMMPA), which aim at sustainably managing marine resources for the benefit of local communities. As we look to the future, Madagascar will need to create MPAs to address the conservation of pelagic species, including the diversity of cetaceans, following in the footsteps of marine conservation initiatives taken by other countries of the south-west Indian Ocean region.

In 2018, Madagascar's current president, Andry Rajoelina, presented a roadmap for the country's future, referred to as the "Initiative for the Emergence of Madagascar". It includes 13 bold objectives, of which Number 10 focuses on sustainable management of the environment and conservation of biodiversity. It is hoped that this new roadmap will play a major role in preventing further erosion of Madagascar's unique biodiversity, and that major habitat restoration projects will result.

What is particularly interesting, indeed amazing, about Madagascar is the fact that we continue to discover new species of very diverse kinds. In spite of the large-scale destruction and periodic socio-political unrest, there has been a huge increase in field and laboratory research in the past few decades, much of it demonstrating how little we really know about this island-continent's biodiversity. Indeed, for the lemurs alone, 52 new species and subspecies have been described since 2000, and quite a few more are in the works. The numbers of new species in other groups of organisms are even more staggering. Over 200 species of amphibians, 107 species of reptiles, one bird, 17 species of small mammals, and 16 species of bats have been discovered and described in Madagascar since 2000.

As exciting as this is, it also presents new conservation challenges. Often when a new species is described it is split off from a previously known form. This results in two taxa, each with smaller ranges. Many of the new species are known only from their type localites (the places where they were first discovered), and several have tiny ranges in areas of extreme habitat fragmentation. Needless to say, as our knowledge of both these new species and the species from which they were split increases, there will inevitably be more species entering the ranks of the Endangered and the Critically Endangered.

Madagascar is often referred to as "the 8th Continent" and this is certainly justified in terms of its incredible biodiversity. As mentioned above, the area of natural habitat remaining on this island-continent is precariously small and continuing to decline. A great deal needs to be done in the immediate future to make sure that the world and the people of Madagascar do not lose Madagascar's incredible biodiversity. We, as a conservation community, cannot do everything, but we can lead on a number of key activities. First of all, we have to do everything possible to protect all remaining intact natural vegetation by ensuring the integrity of the existing protected-area network described above and by adding new protected areas where required. This in itself is a major challenge. Then we have to continue to carry out further ecological and behavioural studies, as well as additional survey work to determine precise geographical distributions and population numbers, especially of the most threatened species and those that have been recently described, as no species is comprehensively known. And we need to continue the ongoing efforts to train a new generation of Malagasy scientists and conservationists to carry the cause into the future.

We also strongly believe that we need to stimulate the growth of ecotourism in Madagascar. Tourism is the world's most rapidly growing industry, and ecotourism is its most rapidly growing component. Given Madagascar's globally unique flora and fauna, and the relative ease with which it can be seen and enjoyed, the country should be one of the world's premier ecotourism destinations. This would help to increase foreign exchange earnings greatly for the country, provide justification for the continued maintenance of the protected area network and, as long as it is done properly, ensure a wide range of benefits to local communities living in close proximity to the country's many protected areas. Indeed, we believe that ecotourism could in short order become Madagascar's number one foreign-exchange earner, but only if the biodiversity upon which it is based is maintained and adequately protected. Fortunately, good models already exist in Madagascar, especially in terms of community guide associations and community-based efforts to create new reserves. These need to scale up as quickly as possible.

The main purpose of this book is to add to the growing body of resources available to facilitate and stimulate mammal ecotourism, including our own lemur field guides and pocket guides, a lemur-watching app, two earlier mammal guides, a bat guide, and a carnivore guide, among other resources. These all make it easier for every visitor to Madagascar to engage in mammal-watching and mammal life-listing. To facilitate this further, in this volume we have included a "Where to watch mammals in Madagascar" section, which highlights some of the best areas to see mammals, and a checklist to begin your own personal Madagascar life-list of those species that you have seen in the wild.

In closing, we sincerely thank Lynx Edicions, and particularly Josep del Hoyo, Amy Chernasky and Albert Martínez-Vilalta, for all that they have done to increase our knowledge of the world's mammals through their stupendous nine-volume series *Handbook of the Mammals of the World* (2009–2019), the above-mentioned and recently published *Illustrated Checklist of the Mammals of the World* (2020), and this new series of regional illustrated checklists that is sure to grow in the future.

References

Albignac, R. (1973). *Mammifères carnivores*. Faune de Madagascar. Vol. 36. ORSTOM and CNRS, Paris.

Anderson, A., Clark, G., Haberle, S., Higham, T., Nowak-Kemp, M., Prendergast, A., Radimilahy, C., Rakotozafy, L.M., Ramilisonina, Schwenninger, J.-L., Virah-Sawmy, M. & Camens, A. (2018). New evidence of megafaunal bone damage indicates late colonization of Madagascar. *PLoS One* **13 (10)**: e0204368. https://doi.org/10.1371/journal.pone.0204368.

Burgin, C.J., Wilson, D.E., Mittermeier, R.A., Rylands, A.B., Lacher, T.E. & Sechrest, W. eds. (2020). *Illustrated Checklist of the Mammals of the World*. Two volumes. Lynx Edicions, Barcelona.

Garbutt, N. (1999). *Mammals of Madagascar*. Yale University Press, New Haven, Connecticut.

Garbutt, N. (2007). *Mammals of Madagascar: a complete guide*. Yale University Press, New Haven, Connecticut.

Glaw, F. & Raselimanana, A.P. (2018). Systematics of terrestrial Malagasy reptiles (Orders Squamata, Testudines and Crocodylia). Pp. 289–327 in: Goodman, Raherilalao & Wohlhauser (2018).

Goodman, S.M. (2011). *Les chauves-souris de Madagascar: Guide de leur distribution, biologie et identification*. Association Vahatra, Antananarivo.

Goodman, S.M. (2012). *Les Carnivora de Madagascar*. Association Vahatra, Antananarivo.

Goodman, S.M. ed. (in press). *The New Natural History of Madagascar*. Princeton University Press, Princeton, New Jersey.

Goodman, S.M. & Benstead, J.P. eds. (2003). *The Natural History of Madagascar*. University of Chicago Press, Chicago, Illinois.

Goodman, S.M., Fratpietro, S. & Tortosa, P. (2020). Insight into the identity and origin of *Scotophilus borbonicus* (E. Geoffroy, 1803). *Acta Chiropt.* **22(1)**: 41–47.

Goodman, S.M. & Jungers, W.L. (2013). *Les animaux et écosystèmes de l'Holocène disparus de Madagascar*. Association Vahatra, Antananarivo.

Goodman, S.M. & Jungers, W.L. (2014). *Extinct Madagascar: picturing the island's past*. University of Chicago Press, Chicago, Illinois.

Goodman, S.M., Raherilalao, M.J. & Wohlhauser, S. eds. (2018). *Les aires protégées terrestres de Madagascar: Leur histoire, description et biote / The Terrestrial Protected Areas of Madagascar: Their history, description, and biota*. Association Vahatra, Antananarivo.

Goodman, S.M. & Ramasindrazana, B. (2018). Systematics of Malagasy bats (order Chiroptera). Pp. 383–394 in: Goodman, Raherilalao & Wohlhauser (2018).

Goodman, S.M. & Soarimalala, V. (2018). Systematics of endemic Malagasy rodents (family Ne-somyidae: subfamily Nesomyinae). Pp. 373–381 in: Goodman, Raherilalao & Wohlhauser (2018).

Goodman, S.M., Soarimalala, V. & Olson, L.E. (2018). Systematics of endemic Malagasy tenrecs (family Tenrecidae). Pp. 363–372 in: Goodman, Raherilalao & Wohlhauser (2018).

Grandidier, A. (1875). *Histoire physique, naturelle et politique de Madagascar*. Volume IX. Histoire Naturelle des Mammifères. Tome IV. Atlas I. Imprimerie Nationale, Paris.

Harper, G.J., Steininger, M.K., Tucker, C.J., Juhn, D. & Hawkins, F. (2007). Fifty years of deforestation and forest fragmentation in Madagascar. *Environ. Conserv.* **34(4)**: 1–9.

Humbert, H. & Cours Darne, G. (1965). Carte internationale du tapis végétal et des conditions écologiques. 3 coupures au 1/1,000,000 de Madagascar. *Trav. Sect. Sci. Tech. Inst. Franç. Pondichéry*, hors sér., 3 maps.

Lowry, P.P., II, Phillipson, P.B., Andriamahefarivo, L., Schtaz, G.E., Rajaonary, F. & Andriambo-lolonera, S. (2018). Flora. Pp. 243–255 in: Goodman, Raherilalao & Wohlhauser (2018).

MEFT, USAID & CI (2009). *Evolution de la couverture de forêts naturelles à Madagascar, 1990–2000–2005*. Ministère de l'Environnement, de Forêts et du Toursime (MEFT), United States Agency for International Development (USAID), and Conservation International (CI), Antananarivo, Washington DC and Arlington, Virginia.

Mitchell, P. (2020). Settling Madagascar: when did people first colonize the world's largest island? *J. Island Coast. Archaeol.* **15(4)**: 576–595.

Mittermeier, R.A., Ganzhorn, J.U., Konstant, W.R., Glander, K., Tattersall, I., Groves, C.P., Rylands, A.B., Hapke, A., Ratsimbazafy, J., Mayor, M.I., Louis, E.E., Jr., Rumpler, Y., Schwitzer, C. & Rasoloarison, R.M. (2008). Lemur diversity in Madagascar. *Int. J. Primatol.* **29**: 1607–1656.

Mittermeier, R.A., Louis, E.E., Jr., Langrand, O., Schwitzer, C., Gauthier, C.-A., Rylands, A.B., Rajaobelina, S., Ratsimbazafy, J., Rasoloarison, R., Hawkins, F., Roos, C., Richardson, M. & Kappeler, P.M. (2014). *Lémuriens de Madagascar*. Muséum national d'Histoire naturelle and Conservation International, Paris and Arlington, Virginia.

Mittermeier, R.A., Louis, E.E., Jr., Richardson, M., Konstant, W.R., Langrand, O., Hawkins, F., Ratsimbazafy, J., Rasoloarison, R., Ganzhorn, J.U., Rajaobelina, S. & Schwitzer, C. (2009). *Lemurs of Madagascar: diurnal and cathemeral lemurs. Pocket Identification Guide*. Conservation International Tropical Pocket Guide Series, Series editors R.A. Mittermeier & A.B. Rylands. Conservation International, Arlington, Virginia.

Mittermeier, R.A., Louis, E.E., Jr., Richardson, M., Konstant. W.R., Langrand, O., Hawkins, F., Ratsimbazafy, J., Rasoloarison, R., Ganzhorn, J.U., Rajaobelina, S. & Schwitzer, C. (2009). *Lemurs of Madagascar: nocturnal lemurs. Pocket Identification Guide*. Conservation International Tropical Pocket Guide Series, Series editors R.A. Mittermeier & A.B. Rylands. Conservation International, Arlington, Virginia.

Mittermeier, R.A., Louis, E.E., Jr., Richardson, M., Schwitzer, C., Langrand, O., Rylands, A.B., Hawkins, F., Rajaobelina, S., Ratsimbazafy, J., Rasoloarison, R., Roos, C., Kappeler, P.M. & MacKinnon, J. (2010). *Lemurs of Madagascar*. 3rd edition. Tropical Field Guide Series. Conservation International, Arlington, Virginia.

Mittermeier, R.A., Myers, N., Robles Gil, P. & Mittermeier, C.G. eds. (1999). *Hotspots: the Earth's biologically richest and most endangered terrestrial ecoregions*. CEMEX, Agrupación Serra Madre, SC, Mexico.

Mittermeier, R.A., Robles Gil, P., Hoffmann, M., Pilgrim, J., Brooks, T., Mittermeier, C.G., Lamoreux, J. & da Fonseca, G.A.B. eds. (2004). *Hotspots Revisited: Earth's biologically richest and most endangered terrestrial ecosystems*. CEMEX, Agrupación Serra Madre, SC, Mexico.

Mittermeier, R.A., Robles Gil, P. & Mittermeier, C.G. eds. (1997). *Megadiversity: Earth's biologically wealthiest nations*. CEMEX, Agrupación Serra Madre, SC, Mexico.

Mittermeier, R.A. & Rylands. A.B. (2017). Biodiversity Hotspots. Pp. 67–75 in: Lacher, T.E., Jr. ed. (2017). *Encyclopedia of the Anthropocene. Volume 3: Biodiversity*. Elsevier, New York.

Mittermeier, R.A., Rylands, A.B. & Wilson, D.E. eds. (2013). *Handbook of the Mammals of the World. Volume 3. Primates*. Lynx Edicions, Barcelona.

Moat, J. & Smith, P. (2007). *Atlas of the Vegetation of Madagascar*. Kew Publishing, Royal Botanic Gardens, Kew.

Petter, J.-J., Albignac, R. & Rumpler, Y. (1977). *Mammifères Lémuriens (Primates Prosimiens)*. Faune de Madagascar Volume 44. ORSTOM and CNRS, Paris.

Rakotoson, J.R. & Razafimahatratra, P.M. (2018). Legal, judicial, and financial aspects of Madagascar's protected areas: past, present and future. Pp. 105–167 in: Goodman, Raherilalao & Wohlhauser (2018).

Safford, R.J. & Hawkins, F. eds. (2013). *The Birds of Africa. Volume VIII. The Malagasy Region*. Christopher Helm, London.

Schwitzer, C., Mittermeier, R.A., Davies, N., Johnson, S., Ratsimbazafy, J., Razafindramanana J., Louis, E.E., Jr., & Rajaobelina, S. eds. (2013). *Lemurs of Madagascar: a strategy for their conservation 2013–2016.* IUCN SSC Primate Specialist Group, Bristol Conservation and Science Foundation, and Conservation International, Bristol and Arlington, Virginia.

Sinclair, J.C. & Langrand, O. (2013). *Birds of the Indian Ocean Islands: Madagascar, Mauritius, Réunion, Rodrigues, Seychelles and the Comoros.* 3rd edition. Struik Publishers, Cape Town.

Soarimalala, V. & Goodman, S.M. (2011). *Les petits mammifères de Madagascar – Guide de leur distribution, biologie et identification.* Association Vahatra, Antananarivo.

Vences, M. & Raselimanana, A.P. (2018). Systematics of Malagasy amphibians (Amphibia: Anura). Pp. 257–288 in: Goodman, Raherilalao & Wohlhauser (2018).

Vieilledent, G., Grinand, C., Rakotomalala, F.A., Ranaivosoa, R., Rakotoarijaona, J.-R., Allnutt, T.F. & Achard, F. (2018). Combining global tree cover loss data with historical national forest cover maps to look at six decades of deforestation and forest fragmentation in Madagascar. *Biol. Conserv.* **222**: 189–197.

Wilson, D.E., Lacher, T.E. & Mittermeier, R.A. eds. (2017). *Handbook of the Mammals of the World. Volume 7. Rodents II.* Lynx Edicions, Barcelona.

Wilson, D.E. & Mittermeier, R.A. eds. (2009). *Handbook of the Mammals of the World. Volume 1. Carnivores.* Lynx Edicions, Barcelona.

Wilson, D.E. & Mittermeier, R.A. eds. (2014). *Handbook of the Mammals of the World. Volume 4. Sea Mammals.* Lynx Edicions, Barcelona.

Wilson, D.E. & Mittermeier, R.A. eds. (2018). *Handbook of the Mammals of the World. Volume 8. Insectivores, Sloths and Colugos.* Lynx Edicions, Barcelona.

Wilson, D.E. & Mittermeier, R.A. eds. (2019). *Handbook of the Mammals of the World. Volume 9. Bats.* Lynx Edicions, Barcelona.

Wright, H.T. & Rakotoarisoa, J.A. (in press). The rise of Malagasy societies: recent developments in the archaelogy of Madagascar. In Goodman (in press).

Background

The compilation of the nine volumes of the *Handbook of the Mammals of the World* (HMW) series saw the first volume published in 2009 and the last in 2019. A major global effort, this series of books involved gathering a wealth of information on all of the world's mammal species in little over a decade. In 2020, the series was summarized in a comprehensive and practical two-volume set entitled *Illustrated Checklist of the Mammals of the World*.

In 2020, using the information compiled for the *Handbook* and the *Illustrated Checklist*, Lynx Edicions launched a series of regional illustrated checklists focused on important geographical areas, to help naturalist-travellers assess with ease how many mammal species are present in a given area, to help them identify what they see, and to enable them to create or complement their own mammal life-lists. These new regional guides provide brief descriptions, including size and weight, habitats used by each species, maps of their geographical ranges, and a colour illustration of each species.

Three regional illustrated checklists have already appeared in this series, *Mammals of the Southern Cone*—Argentina, Chile, Paraguay, and Uruguay (February 2020), *Mammals of South Asia*—Afghanistan, Pakistan, India, Nepal, Bhutan, Bangladesh, and Sri Lanka (June 2020), and *Mammals of China* (October 2020). This fourth guide—*Mammals of Madagascar*—is the first of a series of similar guides to be produced in collaboration with Re:wild.

Using the Illustrated Checklist

Geographical scope

The geographical scope of this guide is the island-continent of Madagascar, with its many unique endemic mammals. A separate small section covers the neighbouring Indian Ocean nations of Mauritius, the Republic of the Seychelles, and the Union of the Comoros (including Grande Comore, Anjouan and Mohéli), as well as the French departments of Mayotte and Réunion. These other Indian Ocean nations and territories have few native land mammals, but we felt it important to include them as well, given their close proximity and affinities to Madagascar. In addition, these Indian Ocean nations and territories have large and often pristine coastal and marine areas where a large proportion of the world's marine mammals can been observed.

Taxonomic treatment

The systematics and taxonomy used in this illustrated checklist follow the HMW series and the two-volume *Illustrated Checklist*, but with additions of new species that have been described since these books were published—which for some groups, such as lemurs, are several. The form known as *Nycteris madagascariensis* has been omitted, as it is no longer considered a valid species. In addition, the two old records previously attributed to it are not now thought to refer to Madagascar.

Species accounts

Each species account begins with its common name in English, its scientific name (genus and species) and its conservation status according to the IUCN Red List of Threatened Species. This book also indicates the common name in French, the European language most used in the region considered.

Also provided are basic biometric body measurements as follows: for non-volant terrestrial mammals, HB = head-body length, T = tail length, and W = weight; for bats, FA = forearm length and W = weight; and for marine mammals, TL = total length and W = weight.

The main body of the text includes a description of the habitat types occupied by the species and the altitudes at which they can be found (if available), and descriptive notes to help in identification.

Finally, there is a colour illustration of the species and a distribution map showing where it occurs in the region. Distributions for terrestrial species are shown in green and for marine species in blue. Usually only one illustration is provided per species, but distinctive subspecies or morphs, as well as sexual differences, may require more than one. Illustrations are not to scale.

The main text of the book is followed by two brief sections, one dealing with the land mammals of the neighbouring islands, and the other covering introduced mammals. There are no maps in the latter section, and IUCN status is likewise omitted. Domestic animals are not included in the book.

Acknowledgements

The HMW series, the *Illustrated Checklist of Mammals*, and this new series would not have been possible without the hard work and dedication of many people, and we are extremely grateful to all of them. In particular, we thank most sincerely those people and organizations that provided support to make the entire HMW series possible, the late Dale and Doris Swanson of Spokane, Washington, and Hayden Lake, Idaho, USA, and Nancy and Dan Jochem of Bozeman, Montana, USA, the daughter and son-in-law of Dale and Doris. Their generous initial contributions helped to make the HMW series a reality. Very special thanks also to Jon Stryker and Slobodan Randjelović for their generous support of lemur conservation in Madagascar, which helped to make this book possible. We are also grateful to Shawn Concannon of Chicago, Illinois, USA, for his long-term support of our species conservation work going back more than 40 years. Additional appreciation to Re:wild and its Emeritus Board Chair Brian Sheth, its President Don Church, and its Global Council member Matt Sechrest for their support of the *Illustrated Checklist* and their overall support to species conservation. Last but not least, we are grateful to Ella Outlaw, Jill Lucena, Stephen D. Nash, and William R. Konstant for their many years of dedication as part of our species conservation team.

Species accounts

TENRECS   Tenrecidae

Lesser Hedgehog Tenrec   *Echinops telfairi*   LC
Petit Tenrec-hérisson

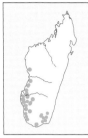

HB 104–165 mm, **T** 13 mm, **W** 50–95 g.
Subhumid, dry and dry spiny forests, open woodland and degraded habitat; occupies arboreal micro-habitats.
Upperparts, including crown, covered in dense, sharp spines, 10–12-mm long. Individually variable from very pale to very dark; spines can be dark over most of length and pale at tip, or dark for the entire length; no noticeable underfur. Underparts, head and limbs covered in short, slightly bristly pale buff hair. Ears prominent.

0–1300 m

Greater Hedgehog Tenrec   *Setifer setosus*   LC
Grand Tenrec-hérisson

HB 140–230 mm, **T** 9–17 mm, **W** 108–350 g.
Humid, subhumid, dry and dry spiny forests, and open woodland; also degraded, agricultural and suburban areas, even with extensive human disturbance. Present in all phytogeographical zones of Madagascar.
Head from between level of eyes and rest of upperparts densely covered in sharp, bristly spines. Spines pale buff for most of length, then dark brown with contrasting white or pale tips; some regional variation in colour. No obvious underfur among spines. Underparts buffy brown; head and limbs well covered with moderately long, soft but bristly hair. Facial vibrissae long and prominent. Ears inconspicuous against spines on head. Lactating female has five pairs of prominent mammae.

0–2250 m

Tailless Tenrec   *Tenrec ecaudatus*   LC
Tenrec commun

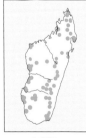

HB 182–350 mm, **W** 148–430 g.
Humid, subhumid, dry and dry spiny forests, open woodland and transitional habitats; also degraded, agricultural and suburban areas. Occurs in all phytogeographical zones of Madagascar.
Male larger than female, with broader head and longer canines. No external tail. Forehead, crown and rest of upperparts covered in mixture of hairs and bristly spines, varying from greyish-brown to reddish-brown or dark brown; spines pale for most of length, with dark band and then pale tip. Mane of longer stiff erectile hairs on crest and mid-dorsal region of body. Underparts sparsely covered with buffy soft, bristly hair; rest of head and limbs covered in short bristly hair. Young buff or light brown below; dark brown above, contrasting with five longitudinal bands of pale spines; broad mid-dorsal band of numerous spines forms stridulating organ; white-tipped spines on nape form low crest.

0–1680 m

Lowland Streaked Tenrec *Hemicentetes semispinosus* LC
Tenrec rayé

0–2050 m

HB 104–176 mm, **W** 76–108 g. Humid forest and open woodland; also degraded, agricultural and suburban areas. No external tail. Dorsal pelage spinous, with sparse underfur and long, sparse guard hairs. Base colour black, with broad pale stripe on midline of head; conspicuous pale fan of spines on top of head and nape; variable pale longitudinal dorsal and lateral stripes on body; a few broad pale spines scattered over upperparts. Contrasting light areas of body show individual variation from reddish-buff to orange and yellow. Stout spines of stridulating organ in posterior mid-dorsal region conspicuous reddish-buff. Underparts bright reddish-brown to yellow, with mixture of sparse soft, bristly hairs and spines. Head and limbs covered in sparse bristly fur. Large naked rhinarium covered with oval scales; ears moderately prominent. Forefeet broad; first and fifth digits reach to or just beyond base of proximal digit; second, third and fourth digits long, with long, shallowly curved stout claws. Hindfeet moderately broad, with long claws on middle three digits.

Highland Streaked Tenrec *Hemicentetes nigriceps* LC
Tenrec à tête noire

1200–2050 m

HB 124–174 mm, **W** 39–129 g. Humid forest, open woodland and montane heathland; also degraded, agricultural and sub-urban areas. Long, pointed snout; lacks external tail. Above, dense bristly black fur, with prominent buff crest of spines on nape, narrow buff stripe on head, and mid-dorsal and lateral buff stripes. Long guard hairs intermixed with sharply pointed spines; those within dark regions dark; those within pale stripes larger, thicker and pale; long, thin spines form prominent transverse band on nape; stout, non-detachable, pale spines form stridulating organ in posterior mid-dorsal region. Sharp demarcation along sides of head and body between black dorsal and pale ventral areas; underparts buff, soft but slightly bristly. Limbs covered in soft, bristly hair, dark buff-brown above, pale buff below. Rhinarium naked and covered with oval scales. Ears partially concealed. Forefeet broad; first and fifth digits short, shorter than or just reaching base of proximal digit; second, third and fourth digits long, with long, shallowly curved, stout claws. Hindfeet moderately broad, with long claws on middle three digits.

Large-eared Tenrec *Geogale aurita* LC
Géogale

HB 51–76 mm, **T** 28–41 mm, **W** 6–9 g.
Subhumid, dry and dry spiny forests, gallery forest and open woodland; also degraded habitats.
Pelage soft and short but not dense; upperparts pale grey to light reddish-brown; sides often tinged yellowish-buff; underside buffy white. Ears large and prominent. Tail c. 50% of head–body length; scaly, with short hairs.

10–870 m

Hova Mole Tenrec *Oryzorictes hova* LC
Oryzoricte taupe

HB 95–124 mm, **T** 38–62 mm, **W** 28–59 g.
Various forest types ranging from humid and transitional humid forests to dry spiny forests; also natural marshes and rice paddies.
Pelage short, soft and dense; upperparts light to dark brown, underparts lighter greyish or buffy brown. Surface of broad rhinarium has very short, sparse hairs. Eyes and ears small and mostly concealed in pelage. Forefeet broad, with five toes; first and fifth digits short and nearly equal in length,
20–1960 m   just reaching base of second and fourth digits; middle three digits have long, stout claws. Hindfeet moderately broad, with fairly long claws on middle three digits. Tail 40–50% of head–body length; pale, and naked apart from sparse bristle hairs.

Four-toed Mole Tenrec *Oryzorictes tetradactylus* DD
Oryzoricte à quatre doigts

HB 106–122 mm, **T** 42–49 mm, **W** 29·5–31 g.
Humid montane forest, heathland and highland marshes.
Fur long, soft and dense, with long brown to dark brown guard hairs; underparts paler. Head brown above, with light buff lateral stripe along margins of mouth; pale below. Rostrum long; rhinarium naked; eyes and ears small, largely concealed in pelage. Forefeet with four toes, pollex absent; second to fourth digits have long, stout claws; fifth digit short, with short claw. Hindfeet have middle three digits with moderately long claws. Tail short relative to head–body length (c. 40%), bicoloured, and covered with long bristle hairs.

2050–2450 m

Dobson's Shrew Tenrec *Nesogale dobsoni* LC
Microgale de Dobson

0–2500 m

HB 87–116 mm,
T 89–128 mm,
W 21–48 g.
Humid and transitional humid to
dry forests; somewhat tolerant of
disturbance, and can be found at forest edge.
Marked seasonal variation in body weight. Pelage soft; above grey-brown
to brown; below grey, with buff to reddish-buff wash. Eyes small; ears
prominent, projecting beyond pelage. Limbs have short hair, usually paler
than upper body. Tail brown above, usually paler below; roughly equal to
head–body length but fluctuates seasonally in girth, becoming distended
with accumulated fat reserves as rainy season approaches and gradually
decreasing in size as reserves depleted.

Talazac's Shrew Tenrec *Nesogale talazaci* LC
Microgale de Talazac

0–2300 m

HB 105–138 mm,
T 103–158 mm,
W 32–47 g.
Humid and
transitional humid to
dry forests; tolerant of some
disturbance.
Pelage short, dense and soft; above dark brown; below grey, with reddish-
buff wash. Eyes and ears small; ears project beyond pelage. Limbs covered
with short hair, similar in colour to belly. Tail generally slightly longer than
head–body length; shows no seasonal incrassation (thickening).

Gracile Shrew Tenrec *Microgale gracilis* LC
Microgale gracile

900–2000 m

HB 85–105 mm, **T** 75–88 mm,
W 20–33 g.
Humid forest; tolerant of some disturbance.
Pelage above dark brown, with buff speckling;
below dark grey, with buff wash. Proboscis very long;
rhinarium large, with naked region extending postero-
dorsally for 4–5 mm; anterior portion reticulated, and striae
on posterior region incomplete. Eyes very small; ears small and partially
concealed by pelage. Forefeet broad, with stout claws that are enlarged on
middle three digits, and noticeably longer than those of hindfeet. Tail nearly
equal to head–body length; dark brown above, pale brown below.

Thomas's Shrew Tenrec *Microgale thomasi* `LC`
Microgale de Thomas

HB 75–112 mm,
T 59–80 mm,
W 20–26 g.
Humid forest.
Fur above speckled dark
rufous brown; below distinctly paler, grey with reddish-buff wash. Middle three digits on forefeet have long claws. Tail c. 90% of head–body length; dark brown above, distinctly paler below, with long, dense scale hairs.

800–2000 m (but recently found at lower and higher elevations)

Dark Shrew Tenrec *Microgale jobihely* `EN`
Microgale du Tsaratanana

HB 53–80 mm,
T 44–57 mm, **W** 7–10 g.
Relatively undisturbed to
slightly disturbed dense humid
forest.
Pelage above dense and soft, a mixture of black and dark reddish-brown hairs or black-tipped reddish-brown hairs, giving agouti appearance; pelage of underparts has finer texture, paler, a mixture of tan-brown and greyish-brown hairs with distinctly grey bases; lateral gradation in colour between dorsal and ventral pelage. Tail 60–90% of head–body length; dark brown above, dark tan-brown below.

1000–1680 m

Cowan's Shrew Tenrec *Microgale cowani* `LC`
Microgale de Cowan

HB 68–87 mm, **T** 54–87 mm,
W 12–17 g.
Humid and transitional humid
to dry forests; also disturbed
forest edge, and rice paddies.
Fur of upperparts speckled brown, individual hairs with dark grey bases and mix of buff and red-brown at tips; underparts grey, with buff wash. Hindfeet brown above, dark grey below; claws on forefeet moderately long. Tail generally less than 90% of head–body length; markedly bicoloured, dark brown above, sharply demarcated from paler reddish-buff below; covered in long scale hairs that partially obscure scales.

530–2525 m

Dryad Shrew Tenrec *Microgale dryas* VU
Microgale dryade

HB 106–114 mm, **T** 68–71 mm, **W** 30–49 g.
Humid forests.
Above grizzled dark reddish- or greyish-brown; below grey, with paler grey wash. Tail c. 60% of head–body length, uniformly grey. Proboscis long; large naked rhinarium extends postero-dorsally for c. 2 mm. Ears large and prominent. Forefeet slightly broadened, with long claws on central three digits.

540–1260 m

Naked-nosed Shrew Tenrec *Microgale gymnorhyncha* LC
Microgale à museau nu

HB 75–101 mm, **T** 59–75 mm, **W** 14–26 g.
Humid forests.
Pelage soft and lustrous, grey-brown above, grey below. Proboscis very long; rhinarium very large, with transversely striated naked region extending postero-dorsally for c. 6–7 mm. Eyes very small; ears small and virtually concealed in pelage. Forefeet broad, with moderately enlarged claws on middle three digits. Tail generally less than 90% of head–body length; grey-brown above, grading into paler below.

595–2525 m

Nasolo's Shrew Tenrec *Microgale nasoloi* VU
Microgale de Nasolo

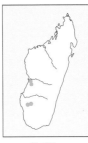

HB 70–81 mm, **T** 50–62 mm, **W** 6–14 g.
Transitional dry deciduous forest, lowland dry deciduous forest, and dry and humid to subhumid forests; also an isolated massif with elements of eastern humid forest and western deciduous forest.
Pelage soft and fine, grey above, grading into darker grey below. Eyes moderately large; ears large and prominent. Tail 60–80% of head–body length; grey, slightly darker above than below, and well covered with long scale hairs.

80–1050 m

Pale Shrew Tenrec *Microgale fotsifotsy* LC
Microgale pâle

HB 59–81 mm, **T** 69–94 mm, **W** 7–15 g.
Humid forest and some transitional dry-to-humid forest.
Pelage soft; above grizzled pale yellowish-brown and grey; below pale grey, with buff or reddish wash. Ears conspicuous and pale. Feet brown, with contrasting pale digits; fifth digit of hindfoot elongated and barely shorter than second. Tail roughly equal to head–body length; bicoloured, grey-brown above, paler grey-buff below, with contrasting pale tip and usually thin pencil of white hairs.

600–2500 m (but recently found at lower elevations)

Shrew-toothed Shrew Tenrec *Microgale soricoides* LC
Microgale soriçoïde

HB 66–103 mm, **T** 81–112 mm, **W** 14–22 g.
Humid forests and transitional humid-spiny to dry forests; tolerant of some disturbance.
Pelage soft, pale grey-brown above, grey-brown below with buff wash. Tail roughly equal to head–body length; brown above, paler buffy brown below; tip white in some individuals.

675–2525 m

Short-tailed Shrew Tenrec *Microgale brevicaudata* LC
Microgale à queue courte

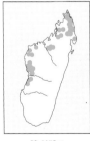

HB 66–88 mm, **T** 30–45 mm, **W** 9–13 g.
Humid forest, dry forest and transitional dry-to-humid forest.
Pelage of upperparts moderately short and coarse, brown with buffy brown speckling; underparts pale greyish-brown. Hindfeet relatively short. Tail less than 60% of head–body length; scale hairs fairly short, and scales are visible.

20–1150 m

33

Grandidier's Shrew Tenrec *Microgale grandidieri* LC
Microgale de Grandidier

HB 60–80 mm, **T** 33–43 mm, **W** 8–10 g. Lowland dry and dry spiny forest, selectively logged and disturbed gallery forest, secondary riparian forest, and dense dry deciduous forest on limestone karst ("tsingy"). Pelage above fine and relatively soft, a mixture of dark brown and lighter brown, giving agouti appearance; separated by well-demarcated line from pelage of underparts, which is finer in texture and uniform medium-grey. Ears short, and covered with fine dark brown or black hairs. Hindfoot relatively short. Tail c. 50% of head–body length.

50–430 m

Drouhard's Shrew Tenrec *Microgale drouhardi* LC
Microgale de Drouhard

HB 63–83 mm, **T** 53–83 mm, **W** 8–14 g. Humid forest and transitional dry-to-humid forest. Marked variation in pelage colour among populations: upperparts brown to dark brown or rufous brown, with well-demarcated, distinctly darker mid-dorsal stripe extending from crown to base of tail; underparts buff to silvery buff or rufous buff. Tail slightly shorter than or equal to head–body length; bicoloured, dark brown above, buff or reddish-buff below; scales readily visible beneath short scale hairs.

530–2500 m

Montane Shrew Tenrec *Microgale monticola* VU
Microgale des montagnes

HB 72–90 mm, **T** 98–117 mm, **W** 12–18 g. Humid forests. Pelage of upperparts dark brown and slightly grizzled; underparts dark brown. Tail c. 120% of head–body length; dark brown above, paler below, with scales clearly visible beneath short scale hairs.

1500–1950 m (down to 500 m in Makira Sud)

Taiva Shrew Tenrec *Microgale taiva* LC
Microgale des Taivas

HB 61–89 mm, **T** 66–95 mm, **W** 10–16 g. Humid forest. Pelage above dark brown, with buffy brown speckling; below grey-brown, with buffy brown wash. Tail generally more than 90% of head–body length; not obviously bicoloured, dark grey-brown above, slightly paler grey below; scales on tail visible beneath short scale hairs.

530–2500 m (but recently found at lower elevations)

Web-footed Shrew Tenrec *Microgale mergulus* VU
Microgale plongeur

HB 116–170 mm, **T** 128–161 mm, **W** 60–110 g. Fast-flowing streams in humid forest; also degraded habitats and rivers bordered by non-native tree plantations. Pelage dense, short and soft; above brown to dark brown, with reddish and yellowish tips to hairs and long black guard hairs; hairs on rump and base of tail have silvery tips; underparts pale grey to yellowish-brown, with silvery sheen. Head short, broad and flattened; muzzle blunt, with pronounced mystacial vibrissae; rhinarium broad, with nostrils positioned dorso-laterally; philtrum well developed; eyes small; ears nearly hidden in fur. Digits of forefeet and hindfeet extensively webbed, and hindfeet fringed with stiff pale hairs. Tail stout proximally, laterally compressed distally; brown above with dark hairs covering scales; longer buffy white hairs on sides and below.

450–2000 m

Pygmy Shrew Tenrec *Microgale parvula* LC
Microgale pygmée

HB 45–65 mm, **T** 47–66 mm, **W** 2–5 g. Humid forest and transitional dry-to-humid forest; generally restricted to pristine forest but tolerant of some disturbance. Very small. Dark brown above; dark grey-brown below; tail and feet uniform dark grey-brown. Tail roughly equal to head–body length; scales visible beneath moderately dense scale hairs.

450–2050 m

35

Major's Long-tailed Shrew Tenrec *Microgale majori* `LC`
Microgale de Major

HB 52–66 mm, **T** 102–134 mm, **W** 5–8 g. Humid to sub-humid forests; tolerant of some disturbance.

Small, with very long, partially prehensile tail. Upperparts dark brown, with reddish-brown wash; below dark grey, with reddish-buff wash. Fifth digit of hindfoot elongated, only slightly shorter than second digit. Tail over 170% of head–body length; grey-brown above, clearly demarcated from reddish-buff below; scales on dorsal surface of distal portion are broad and naked.

800–2500 m

Lesser Long-tailed Shrew Tenrec *Microgale longicaudata* `LC`
Microgale à longue queue

HB 59–80 mm, **T** 136–158 mm, **W** 6–11 g.
Humid forest; tolerant of some disturbance.

Small, with very long, partially prehensile tail. Pelage above reddish-brown; below grey, with reddish-buff or buff wash. Digits of both forefeet and hindfeet elongated; fifth hind digit only slightly shorter than second. Tail typically more than twice head–body length; grey-brown above, clearly distinguished from reddish-buff below; distal portion naked, with broad transverse scales on dorsal surface.

530–2500 m

Jenkins's Shrew Tenrec *Microgale jenkinsae* `EN`
Microgale de Jenkins

HB 59–62 mm, **T** 79–81 mm, **W** 5 g. Dense under-storey of par-tially disturbed lowland dry spiny forest.

Very small. Pelage above relatively dense and soft, a mixture of black and tan-brown hairs giving agouti appearance; grades into paler underparts of pale tan to silvery white hairs. Ears notably large relative to body size. Tail 130–140% of head–body length; dark brown above, tan-brown below.

0–80 m

Greater Long-tailed Shrew Tenrec *Microgale principula* LC
Grand Microgale

HB 69–89 mm,
T 144–171 mm,
W 9–14 g.
Humid forest.
Small to medium-sized,
with very long, partially
prehensile tail. Pelage reddish-
brown above, grey with buff wash below; colour
variable, as is contrast between upper- and underparts. Digits
elongated; fifth hind digit only slightly shorter than second. Tail
normally more than twice head–body length; tip has transversely
broadened naked scales covering dorsal surface.

500–1875 m (but recently
found at lower elevations)

Least Shrew Tenrec *Microgale pusilla* LC
Petit Microgale

HB 51–63 mm, **T** 62–85 mm, **W** 3–5 g.
Humid forest, wet grassland and marshy habitats; tolerant of some disturbance.
Very small, with long tail, 130–160% of head–body length. Pelage above
soft, grizzled reddish-brown; below grey, with buffy wash.

530–1670 m (but recently
found at higher elevations)

DUGONG Dugongidae

Dugong *Dugong dugon* VU
Dugong

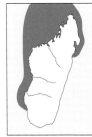

TL 200–330 cm, **W** to at least 570 kg.
Exploits tidal cycles to access intertidal seagrass meadows.
Eyes small, muzzle points downwards; hindlimbs absent, tail fluke whale-
like, forelimbs paddle-like without nails. Skin smooth with sparse hair; dark
grey above (may appear brownish), often with white patches and extensive
scarring; paler below.

Grey Mouse Lemur   *Microcebus murinus*   LC
Microcèbe murin

0–800 m

HB 12–14 cm, **T** 13–14·5 cm, **W** c. 60 g. Primary and secondary lowland tropical dry forest and subarid thorn scrub, as well as semi-humid deciduous, gallery, spiny and eastern littoral forest. Occupies fine-branch niche, with dense foliage and abundant fine branches and narrow lianas. Prefers to sleep in tree holes.

Large mouse lemur. Above brownish-grey with various reddish tones; flanks pale grey to beige; discrete dull beige or whitish-beige patches along parts of belly. Pale white patch between eyes; some individuals have dark orbital markings. Ears long and fleshy compared with shorter, more concealed ears of *M. rufus*. Furred portions of hands and feet off-white. Tail barely longer than head–body length. Male consistently heavier than female during breeding, but opposite is true during rest of year.

Ganzhorn's Mouse Lemur   *Microcebus ganzhorni*   EN
Microcèbe de Ganzhorn

No measurements available. Evergreen littoral forest. Small mouse lemur. Above reddish-brown, below whitish. Ears pale; eyes surrounded by dark rings; conspicuous white stripe from nose to forehead, passing between eyes.

Bemanasy Mouse Lemur   *Microcebus manitatra*   CR
Microcèbe pionnier

HB 12·5 cm, **T** 15 cm, **W** 58 g. Humid forest; perhaps also littoral forest. Relatively large mouse lemur with long tail, long ears and shortish hindfeet. Above uniform greyish-brown; below greyish-beige, with dark underfur.

Grey-brown Mouse Lemur *Microcebus griseorufus* LC
Microcèbe gris-roux

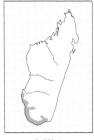

0–250 m

HB 12–13 cm, **T** 14–15 cm, **W** 40–50 g.
Spiny forest and dry thorn scrub; also gallery forest.
In Berenty Reserve, found in spiny forest patches
but not in adjacent gallery forest, which is
occupied by *M. murinus*; but they co-occur in
Beza-Mahafaly and in Mikea Forest.
Medium-sized, with relatively robust skull. Fur
above pale grey, divided by cinnamon-
coloured midline stripe that runs
from crown or shoulders to tip of
tail; underparts pale greyish-
white on forward portion,
with belly greyer. Tail mainly
cinnamon above, beige below. Weight varies by season
and gender.

Ambarijeby Mouse Lemur *Microcebus danfossi* VU
Microcèbe de Danfoss

0–780 m

HB 12·7–13·6 cm, **T** 16·5–17·3 cm, **W** 63 g.
Intact and degraded forest fragments.
Probably largest mouse lemur; only slightly larger
than very similar *M. bongolavensis* and *M. ravelo-
bensis*. Fur short and dense, grey at hair base
and variably coloured at tip; back maroon tinged
orange, sometimes with faint dorsal line, below
creamy white. Colour of head varies. some individuals
(perhaps young) have uniformly rufous to brown head,
whereas others have this colour restricted to triangular
patch over eyes, with pale greyish crown; distinct white
stripe between eyes; ears rufous. Hands and feet sparsely
haired and white. Tail same colour as back; fur short and
dense on proximal part, but longer and sparser at tip.

Bongolava Mouse Lemur *Microcebus bongolavensis* EN
Microcèbe du Bongolava

HB 9–12·2 cm, **T** 14·7–17·1 cm, **W** c. 54 g.
Dense primary forest fragments in mountainous areas.
Large reddish mouse lemur. Fur short and dense,
above maroon tinged orange (sometimes with faint
dorsal line), below creamy white. Head variable:
some individuals (perhaps young) have uniformly
rufous to brown head, whereas others have this
colour restricted to triangular patch over eyes, with
pale greyish crown; distinct white stripe between
eyes; ears rufous. Hands and feet sparsely haired
and white. Tail same colour as body; fur short and
dense on proximal part but longer and sparser at tip.

Golden-brown Mouse Lemur *Microcebus ravelobensis* VU
Microcèbe doré

0–500 m

HB 12–13 cm, **T** 15–17 cm, **W** 57 g.
Dry deciduous lowland forest; sometimes degraded patches of forest. Apparently prefers forests with lower canopy and more lianas than those inhabited by *M. murinus*, and uses tree holes less often.
Large mouse lemur. Fur short and dense. Above, including crown and ears, rufous and mottled; below mottled or bicoloured yellow to whitish; mid-dorsal stripe poorly defined. Regions between eyes prominently pale greyish changing to cinnamon towards crown; eye-rings dark brown. Ears long and naked. Tail brown, darker at tip.

Anjiahely Mouse Lemur *Microcebus macarthurii* EN
Microcèbe de MacArthur

HB 11–12 cm, **T** 14·7 cm, **W** c. 53 g.
Lowland rainforest.
Large mouse lemur. Fur above short and dense, reddish-brown with broad dark rufous midline stripe from head to tail; paler reddish on outer upper legs and arms; below yellowish-orange, with creamy white throat and genital region. Head rufous, turning orange on cheeks; dark brownish around eyes, with white interocular stripe characteristic of genus. Ears darker rufous. Hands and feet sparsely haired; greyish-white. Tail densely furred; reddish-brown, darker above than below, and middle brown towards tip.

Jonah's Mouse Lemur *Microcebus jonahi* NE
Microcèbe de Jonah

40–360 m

HB c. 13 cm, **T** 13 cm, **W** 66 g.
Primary and degraded forest; mostly found in stands of cardamom (*Aframomum angustifolium*) 2–4 m high.
Large mouse lemur with small ears. Fur above short and dense, reddish-brown, with dark midline stripe sometimes present; below white, slightly tinged yellowish, well demarcated from dorsal coloration. Head rufous, with darker brownish around eyes, and white interocular stripe reaching forehead; cheeks lighter and browner, less rufous, becoming whitish towards throat. Ears rufous like head. Hands and feet sparsely haired whitish-grey. Tail densely furred; reddish-brown, like upperparts.

Marohita Mouse Lemur *Microcebus marohita* `CR`
Microcèbe de Marohita

HB 13·2–14 cm, **T** 13·3–14·5 cm, **W** 64–89 g.
Rainforest.
Large, heavy mouse lemur, with long tail, long hindfeet and short ears. Fur above long and soft, rufous with ill-defined dark midline stripe from shoulders to base of tail; below whitish-beige, greyer on flanks, sharply separated from dorsal colouring. Patch between eyes dull white to pale pinkish-buff. Hands and feet sparsely haired whitish-grey. Tail darker towards tip.

Gerp's Mouse Lemur *Microcebus gerpi* `CR`
Microcèbe du Gerp

29–230 m

HB c. 8·4 cm, **T** c. 14·8 cm, **W** 68 g.
Lowland primary and secondary rainforest. Above greyish-brown with diffuse broad rufous midline; below pale grey to creamy white (including scrotum); outer arms and legs darker than rest of body. Head rufous brown, darker around eyes, with distinct white stripe between eyes. Ears small but prominent; dark brown towards edges. Skin on hands and feet pinkish-brown. Tail long and densely furred, brownish-grey, darker above than below; can store body fat.

Tavaratra Mouse Lemur *Microcebus tavaratra* `VU`
Microcèbe du Nord

20–250 m

HB 12–14 cm, **T** 15–16 cm, **W** 54 g.
Tropical dry deciduous lowland and gallery forest.
Fur long and dense; brownish-black above with distinct brownish midline stripe extending from crown or shoulders to base of tail; below typically a mixture of whitish-beige and grey. Crown and ears rufous; area between eyes greyish-white; distinct black markings below eyes. Fur on hands and feet greyish-white.

41

Tanosy Mouse Lemur *Microcebus tanosi* EN
Microcèbe de Tanosy

HB 11·6–14 cm, **T** 11·5–15 cm, **W** 48–60 g.
Littoral forest, especially around forest edge.
Relatively large mouse lemur. Fur above dark brownish
with reddish head and diffuse dark dorsal stripe reaching
base of tail; below pale greyish-beige, paler on flanks.
Distinct white stripe between eyes. Skin on hands and feet
clay-coloured.

Jolly's Mouse Lemur *Microcebus jollyae* EN
Microcèbe de Jolly

HB c. 13 cm, **T** c. 12 cm,
W 49 g.
Lowland coastal rainforest.
Above uniform greyish-brown
on body and head; below
greyish. Small white
patch between eyes.

Nosy Boraha Mouse Lemur *Microcebus boraha* DD
Microcèbe de Boraha

0–70 m

HB 13·6 cm, **T** 14·1–14·8 cm, **W** 56·5 g.
No information on habitat.
Relatively large mouse lemur with long tail, long hindfeet
and short ears. Fur above reddish, with indistinct
mid-dorsal stripe; below white with reddish
tinges.

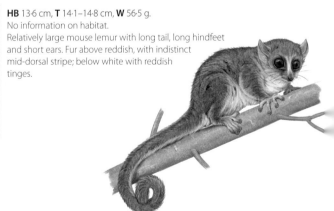

Simmons's Mouse Lemur *Microcebus simmonsi* EN
Microcèbe de Simmons

HB 9·2 cm, **T** 14·2 cm, **W** 42–64·8 g.
Lowland rainforest.
Large, robust species. Upperparts, head and forelimbs dark reddish-brown to orange-brown, sometimes with mid-dorsal stripe; below greyish-white to white. White patch between eyes; hairs on middle of crown have black tips.

Nosy Be Mouse Lemur *Microcebus mamiratra* EN
Microcèbe de Claire

HB 12·7 cm, **T** 14·3 cm, **W** 58 g.
Primary and secondary forest.
Fur short and dense; upper body, head and ears light reddish-brown, brighter on back and crown; sometimes a faint light greyish-brown dorsal midline; below white to creamy white. Whitish midline stripe on front of muzzle, wider and more diffuse between eyes. Hands and feet sparsely haired, grey or white. Tail rufous brown on proximal part changing gradually to dark brown at tip.

Margot Marsh's Mouse Lemur *Microcebus margotmarshae* EN
Microcèbe de Marsh

HB 11–12 cm, **T** 14 cm, **W** 49 g.
Dry forest.
Medium-sized mouse lemur. Fur above and on tail mostly reddish-orange, but with grey tones; below white to cream. Most of head bright reddish-orange; light brown fur covers muzzle and area around eyes, with small, clearly marked white patch on ridge of nose between eyes; ears small.

Sambirano Mouse Lemur *Microcebus sambiranensis* EN
Microcèbe du Sambirano

HB 11–12 cm, **T** 13·5–14·5 cm, **W** 45 g.
Humid and dry forest; occasionally disturbed habitats and forests bordering farmland. Medium-sized mouse lemur. Fur long and dense, bright reddish-cinnamon above with poorly defined amber midline stripe extending from just beyond shoulders to tip of tail; below dull whitish-beige. Pale patch between eyes; dark eye-rings; crown and ears amber.

300–1600 m

Montagne d'Ambre Mouse Lemur *Microcebus arnholdi* VU
Microcèbe d'Arnhold

HB c. 12·6 cm, **T** 10·6–13·6 cm, **W** 45 g.
Montane rainforest. Medium-sized mouse lemur. Above, a mixture of dark brown, red and grey, with tail dark brown near tip; dark brown dorsal midline stripe runs to base of tail; below white to cream with grey tones. Head mainly red, with dark brown on muzzle and around eyes; white nose ridge.

50–990 m

Mittermeier's Mouse Lemur *Microcebus mittermeieri* EN
Microcèbe de Mittermeier

HB c. 8 cm, **T** c. 12 cm, **W** 46 g.
Lowland and highland rainforest and subhumid forest. One of the smallest eastern-rainforest mouse lemurs. Head and upperparts light reddish-brown to rust, with orange tint at base of forelimbs and hindlimbs; below whitish-brown. White rostral patch stretches to slightly above eyes; yellow area below eyes, extending onto chin and throat. Tail brown above, with darker brown mid-dorsal stripe and black tip.

0–1760 m

Goodman's Mouse Lemur *Microcebus lehilahytsara* VU
Microcèbe de Goodman

825–1500 m

HB c. 9 cm, **T** c. 10 cm, **W** 45–48 g.
Rainforest; also, in lower numbers, old *Eucalyptus* plantations, if understorey sufficiently developed to permit travel without descending to ground.
Small mouse lemur. Fur short and dense, bright maroon tinged orange on back, head and tail; creamy white below. Distinct white stripe between eyes, reaching lower forehead. Ears short and round. Scrotum furred.

Madame Berthe's Mouse Lemur *Microcebus berthae* CR
Microcèbe de Berthe

0–150 m

HB 9–9.5 cm, **T** 13–14 cm, **W** 31 g.
Dry deciduous lowland forest.
Smallest mouse lemur, and probably world's smallest primate. Fur short and dense, cinnamon and yellow-ochre above, with distinct darker midline stripe extending from just behind shoulders to tip of tail; brighter on head than on back, with crown, ears and tail tawny; underparts pale yellow-brown to pale grey; furred portions of hands and feet dull beige. Narrow black bands surround eyes; dull white patch above nose; ears very short. Male heavier than female during breeding, but opposite is true during rest of year.

Peters's Mouse Lemur *Microcebus myoxinus* VU
Microcèbe pygmée

0–900 m

HB 12–13 cm, **T** 14–15 cm, **W** 42 g.
Tropical dry deciduous lowland forest; locally along margins of heavily degraded deciduous forest and grassland. Also mangrove forests (Baie de Baly).
Fur short, rufous brown above, tinged orange; pale yellow-brown to pale grey below. Distinct, dark median stripe down back; white stripe from forehead to nose; pale cinnamon patch near eyes darkens to reddish behind eyes, with tawny crown and ears; dark eyebrows prominent. Ears relatively short. Furred portions of hands and feet whitish-grey to whitish-beige. Tail relatively long, densely furred, and darker towards tip.

Rufous Mouse Lemur *Microcebus rufus* VU
Microcèbe roux

0–2000 m

HB 12 cm, **T** 10·9–12·5 cm, **W** 44 g.
Tropical moist lowland and montane forest; occasionally adjacent secondary forest formations, bamboo forest, old plantations and *Eucalyptus* groves.
Lightly built species, probably smallest of eastern-rainforest mouse lemurs. Head and forelimbs reddish-brown, blending into greyish-brown upperparts and tail; black midline stripe runs down back; underparts greyish-white. Conspicuous white rostral patch does not extend past level of eyes. Ears naked and short, half-hidden in fur of head. Tail relatively long.

Coquerel's Giant Mouse Lemur *Mirza coquereli* EN
Microcèbe de Coquerel

0–700 m

HB 25 cm, **T** 31–32 cm, **W** c. 299–317 g.
Lowland dry deciduous forest fragments with dense underbrush; also gallery forest and coffee plantations. Prefers forest near water (e.g. semi-permanent ponds) with canopy height of up to 20 m.
Above rich brown or grey-brown, with rose or yellow shades often present; below, grey hair bases visible beneath rusty or yellow tips. Ears large, naked and oval. Tail longer than body, and thin but long-haired, giving slightly bushy appearance; darker towards tip. Male averages slightly heavier than female.

Northern Giant Mouse Lemur *Mirza zaza* VU
Microcèbe zaza

HB c. 27 cm, **T** 27–28 cm, **W** 290 g.
Lowland dry deciduous forest fragments with dense underbrush, transitional subhumid forest, gallery forest and abandoned cashew (*Anacardium*, introduced) orchards; also old banana plantations.
Slightly smaller than *M. coquereli*, with relatively shorter, rounded ears and shorter tail. Body covered in short greyish-brown fur, becoming distinctly greyer below. Tail long and bushy, darker towards tip.

Hairy-eared Dwarf Lemur *Allocebus trichotis* EN
Allocèbe

HB 13–16 cm, **T** 14–20 cm, **W** 79 g.
Primary moist tropical lowland and
mid-altitude rainforest; mainly below
1000 m, but some populations montane.
Usually found in tangles of brush or lianas,
foraging in lower canopy. Appears to tolerate
moderate levels of human activity.
Body rosy brownish-grey above, greyish-
white below. Black areas immediately around
eyes; pale white stripe sometimes present on
nose, from between eyes to tip; cheeks white.
Conspicuous plumes of wavy dark brown hair cover rather small ears. Tail
long; same colour as upper body, becoming darker and bushier at end.

0–1600 m

Sibree's Dwarf Lemur *Cheirogaleus sibreei* CR
Chirogale de Sibree

HB 20·5–23·5 cm, **T** 22–26·5 cm, **W** 272 g.
High-altitude rainforest.
Greyish-fawn above and on cap, with or
without darker dorsal median line; below pale grey to creamy, continuing
onto sides of neck and flanks and
along outsides of thighs. Distinct,
broad black eye-rings; muzzle
slightly greyer than back;
rhinarium usually pink; ears
naked and dark, with sparse hair
on inner and outer surfaces. Hands
and feet pink below, grey-brown above.

1300–2000 m

Ankarana Dwarf Lemur *Cheirogaleus shethi* EN
Chirogale de Sheth

HB 16·4–17·5 cm, **T** 15·5 cm, **W** 101–125 g.
Dry deciduous, semi-humid and littoral forests; also
man-altered habitats (e.g. vanilla plantations) and
savanna scrub forest.
Small. Upperparts, crown and outer part of limbs
light grey, with no dark median line down spine;
underside and inner part of limbs white. No
obvious mask, but eyes with dark surrounding
rings; nose pink. Ears sparsely furred and
dark. Hands and feet pale pink.

15–540 m

47

Thomas's Dwarf Lemur *Cheirogaleus thomasi* EN
Chirogale de Thomas

No measurements available.
Dry to wet littoral forests, requiring large trees for hibernation; sometimes feeds in *Eucalyptus* plantations. Small. Similar overall to *C. medius*, but with less contrasting coloration. Tail said to be slightly longer than head–body length.

0–40 m

Fat-tailed Dwarf Lemur *Cheirogaleus medius* VU
Petit Chirogale

0–800 m

HB 17–23 cm, **T** 19–27 cm, **W** c. 135 g.
Primary and secondary dry deciduous, gallery, evergreen humid, and transitional subhumid forests. One of the smaller members of the genus. Upper body pale frosted fawn-grey, with broad but indistinct brown dorsal stripe; underside broadly creamy or yellowish (somewhat yellower towards midline), with partial white collar around throat, sharply marked, extending well up on sides of neck. White median facial stripe; eye-rings dark brown. Hands and feet white; ears naked. Tail length roughly equal to head–body length. Weight varies seasonally, being greater just before onset of seasonal torpor.

Greater Dwarf Lemur *Cheirogaleus major* VU
Grand Chirogale

0–1800 m

HB 23–27 cm, **T** 29–30 cm, **W** 314 g (Nov) to 414 g (Feb).
Primary and secondary eastern lowland rainforest and montane forest; also, marginally, western dry forest; sometimes found in coffee and lychee plantations. Generally occurs at average height of 12·2 m in canopy; prefers large trees for feeding, travelling and resting. Largest member of genus. Fur dense, above greyish-brown, below dark creamy grey with traces of yellow; dorsal midline stripe, if present, dark reddish-brown and indistinct. Muzzle rounded and dark; face pale, up to level of eyes. Eye-rings dark but poorly marked; ears naked or very sparsely furred, and not darkly pigmented. Tail longer than head–body length.

Sabin's Dwarf Lemur *Cheirogaleus andysabini* `EN`
Chirogale de Sabin

540–1075 m

Body 18·2 cm, **T** 27·1 cm, **W** 310 g.
Rainforest.
Upperparts, head and outside of limbs rufous brown; underparts white. Face brighter tan; eyes surrounded by blackish-brown rings; white patch on upper nose, between eyes. Ears small and dark.

Groves's Dwarf Lemur *Cheirogaleus grovesi* `DD`
Chirogale de Groves

700–1000 m

Body 17·1 cm, **T** 27·7 cm, **W** 404 g.
Montane rainforest.
Fur rufous brown on upperparts, crown and outside of limbs; rufous grey below, becoming whitish on chin and throat. Eyes surrounded by brownish-black rings; white patch on upper nose, between eyes.

Lavasoa Dwarf Lemur *Cheirogaleus lavasoensis* `EN`
Chirogale du Lavasoa

0–1225 m

HB 26·7 cm, **T** 27 cm, **W** 297 g.
Known only from small forest fragments. Above reddish-brown on head merging to greyish-brown towards base of tail; outside of limbs grey-brown to reddish-brown, tail grey-brown; below pale creamy. Eyes surrounded by sharply delineated broad black rings. Ears dark on both surfaces.

Crossley's Dwarf Lemur *Cheirogaleus crossleyi* `VU`
Chirogale de Crossley

HB 22–26 cm, **T** 21–27 cm, **W** 370–458 g.
Rainforest on plateau margins; also plantations and degraded forest.
Similar to *C. major*, but slightly shorter and heavier, with more pointed nose and smaller teeth; head low and flat. Fur generally russet above, with creamy grey underparts and orange-yellow throat; no trace of dorsal stripe. Mid-facial zone yellowish, extending above eyes and onto

0–1800 m

sides of nose; blackish eye-rings. Ears heavily pigmented and covered in black fur inside and out (unlike *C. major*). Tail roughly equal to head–body length.

Masoala Fork-marked Lemur *Phaner furcifer* `EN`
Phaner à fourche

No precise measurements available.
Tropical moist lowland forest.
Largest and darkest member of the genus, with notably long, dense pelage. Above dark brown, below creamy buff to buffy grey. Crown markings thick, black and distinct; dorsal midline stripe does not reach base of tail. Cheeks and back of nose greyish-yellow; ears large and bare, with rounded tips. Hands and feet dark. Tail c. 150% of head–body length; bushy, becoming dark towards tip.

0–1000 m

Pale Fork-marked Lemur *Phaner pallescens* `EN`
Phaner pâle

HB 23–29 cm, **T** 29–37 cm, **W** 333 g.
Secondary lowland tropical dry deciduous forest; can adapt to exotic tree plantations.
Palest and perhaps smallest of fork-marked lemurs; broad muzzle and small teeth. Upper body pale fawn-grey with silvery sheen; underside whitish to pale yellowish. Crown fork and dorsal midline stripe poorly defined, but stripe reaches rump. Hands and feet only slightly darker than body. Tail dark for half to three-quarters of its length.

0–800 m

Sambirano Fork-marked Lemur *Phaner parienti* `EN`
Phaner de Pariente

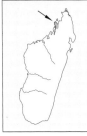

0–800 m

HB c. 24 cm, **T** c. 40 cm, **W** c. 360 g.
Tall lowland tropical moist forest; can survive in remnant forest canopies shading coffee plantations.
Larger than *P. pallescens*, with larger teeth and tail at least as long as head–body length. Fur thick and dense; above dark brown, below buff, often with reddish tints. Crown fork broad, black, well defined and continuous with dorsal midline stripe, which extends to base of tail. Distal third of tail dark, but occasionally tipped white.

Montagne d'Ambre Fork-marked Lemur *Phaner electromontis* `EN`
Phaner de la Montagne d'Ambre

50–1000 m

HB c. 27 cm, **T** c. 34·5 cm, **W** c. 390 g.
Secondary tropical moist forest, dry deciduous forest and gallery forest. Large, with tail considerably longer than head–body length. Fur light grey above and below, with well-defined thick black crown fork and dorsal stripe, latter extending to rump. Hands and feet slightly darker than body; tail dark on distal third.

SPORTIVE LEMURS Lepilemuridae

Masoala Sportive Lemur *Lepilemur scottorum* EN
Lépilémur des Scott

HB 25–28 cm, **T** 25–29 cm, **W** 880 g.
Primary lowland rainforest; sometimes also in selectively logged forest.
Fur long and thick, uniform reddish-brown above and below, with diffuse black midline stripe down to middle of back. Face whitish-grey; cheeks and eyebrows white. Hands and feet reddish-brown. Tail reddish-brown at base, turning progressively brownish-grey towards black tip.

Mananara-Nord Sportive Lemur *Lepilemur hollandorum* CR
Lépilémur des Holland

275–375 m

HB 29·3–33·7 cm, **T** 26·8–29·4 cm, **W** c. 1 kg.
Lowland rainforest.
Large. Fur on head and shoulders and down to mid-back mottled reddish-grey, becoming paler greyish-brown towards base of tail. Head with faint dark brown to black mid-dorsal stripe or inverted Y-shaped pattern that progresses to lower half of back. Face generally grey, neck lighter brown to blonde; fleshy ears protrude. Underparts pale grey, with darker undertones. Hands and feet greyish-brown. Tail dark brown to black towards tip.

Seal's Sportive Lemur *Lepilemur seali* VU
Lépilémur de Seal

980–1050 m

HB c. 27 cm, **T** c. 26 cm, **W** c. 950 g.
Rainforest.
Extremely long, thick fur. Fur uniform pale chocolate-brown to reddish-brown above, lighter brownish-grey below, with cream-tipped hairs along lateral border. Face light brownish-grey, with yellow to white collar on neck. Hands and feet light greyish-brown. Tail contrasting brownish-grey, occasionally with hairs tipped white.

Wright's Sportive Lemur *Lepilemur wrightae* EN
Lépilémur de Wright

HB 24–26 cm, **T** 25–26 cm, **W** 1·1 kg.
Rainforest.
Large sportive lemur, notable for its sexual dimorphism, so far as is known unique in the genus. Fur of both sexes diffuse reddish-brown and grey above, paler greyish-brown below. Head of male same colour as back, but that of female sharply contrasting rather uniform grey; some females may have slight colour change around face, giving mask-like appearance. Ears (both sexes) with minimal to short fur, and paler than rest of head.

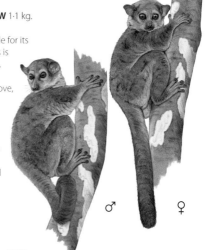

♂   ♀

Andohahela Sportive Lemur *Lepilemur fleuretae* EN
Lépilémur de Fleurette

HB 24–26 cm, **T** 27–30 cm, **W** 800 g.
Lowland rainforest.
Fur predominantly grey above, paler brownish-grey below, with greyish-brown mixture along bases of limbs and some light brown along lateral edges of belly. Fur noticeably paler over eyelids than on rest of face. Diffuse dark stripe runs along midline, from forecrown roughly halfway down back. Tail reddish-grey at base, darker grey towards tip.

Weasel Sportive Lemur *Lepilemur mustelinus* VU
Lépilémur mustelin

HB 21–25 cm, **T** 25–29 cm, **W** c. 1 kg.
Primary and secondary humid rainforest.
Long, dense fur and relatively short tail. Upper body chestnut-brown, underside paler; often vague dorsal or crown stripe; tail darkens towards tip. Face dark grey or brown, with brown eyes; cheeks and throat whitish; naked ears project beyond fur. Bright orange morph exists. Female c. 10% heavier than male.

Betsileo Sportive Lemur *Lepilemur betsileo* EN
Lépilémur du Betsileo

HB c. 25 cm, **T** c. 28 cm, **W** 1–1·2 kg.
Rainforest.
Large sportive lemur, appearing mainly greyish to reddish-brown; fur is mixture of dark to light grey and reddish-brown, darker above than below. Chin white, rest of face grey; fur within ear noticeably paler and bordered by dark brown to black along outer edge. Tail black, contrasting sharply with body.

Manombo Sportive Lemur *Lepilemur jamesorum* CR
Lépilémur des James

HB 26 cm, **T** 30 cm, **W** 964 g.
Moist low-altitude coastal rainforest.
Large species with short, smooth fur. Generally brown above, with black midline stretching from crown down onto tail; paler greyish-brown below and on underside of limbs. Face forms dark brown mask above whitish-grey area from chin and throat to ears. Ears large and cup-shaped, grey above with black borders and usually a small creamy patch below. Tail brown at base, gradually becoming darker brown to black towards tip.

White-footed Sportive Lemur *Lepilemur leucopus* EN
Lépilémur à pieds blancs

0–300 m

HB 19–26 cm, **T** 22–26 cm, **W** 580 g.
Mainly spiny Didiereaceae forest and bushy areas; also gallery, riparian and subtropical dry lowland forests.
One of the smallest sportive lemurs. Above, including head, pale grey tending towards brown on shoulders, upper forelimbs and upper thighs; below greyish-white (often conspicuous along flanks and around base of tail, even when the lemur is clinging to tree). Face greyish-brown; eyes with whitish spectacles; ears relatively large and rounded, with whitish tufts at bases. Tail greyish-brown.

Petter's Sportive Lemur *Lepilemur petteri* EN
Lépilémur de Petter

145–170 m

HB c. 23 cm, **T** c. 24 cm, **W** 630 g.
Mainly deciduous thickets and thorn scrub, as well as some gallery forest.
Small sportive lemur. Fur grey to greyish-brown above, whitish-grey below, with diffuse brownish-grey on fore-part of thighs and along dorsal midline. Face grey with lighter circular patches around eyes and under chin; ears trimmed in lighter fur, highlighting dark brownish-grey inner lining.

Bemaraha Sportive Lemur *Lepilemur randrianasoloi* EN
Lépilémur de Randrianasolo

45–140 m

HB c. 28·7 cm, **T** c. 27·6 cm, **W** 775 g.
Dry forest.
Similar to *L. aeeclis* but a little slighter, with longer, narrower head (most pronounced in male). Overall coloration light grey, with mixture of reddish-brown and grey on dorsal surface of forearms, hindlimbs, shoulders and back. Face lighter grey, producing mask-like appearance; darker line mid-dorsally on head. Tail paler red.

Antafia Sportive Lemur *Lepilemur aeeclis* EN
Lépilémur d'Antafia

HB 21–24 cm, **T** 24–25 cm, **W** 850 g.
Dry forest.
Rather similar to *L. ahmansonorum*, but slightly more
heavily built (the two are geographically close but do
not overlap). Coloration very variable (perhaps related to
age), but generally grey or reddish-grey on back and tail,
and light or dark grey below. Face grey, sometimes with
darker patch on forehead; darker stripes from above eyes
join on centre of crown and continue down back to tail; ears
rounded and protruding.

10–65 m

Red-tailed Sportive Lemur *Lepilemur ruficaudatus* CR
Lépilémur à queue rousse

HB 24–30 cm, **T** 24–28 cm, **W** 771 g.
Subtropical and tropical dry lowland deciduous
forest; also gallery forest and bushland.
Fur above pale greyish-brown, with reddish-chestnut
tinges on shoulders and forelimbs; below pale grey,
with throat and face cream-coloured. Eyes yellow,
but may become brown with age; ears rounded
and prominent. Tail reddish-brown, often with
white tip.

0–900 m

Zombitse Sportive Lemur *Lepilemur hubbardi* EN
Lépilémur de Hubbard

HB 23–24 cm, **T** c. 24 cm, **W** 990 g.
Dry forest.
Medium-sized to large sportive lemur. Fur above dark
reddish-brown around shoulders and upper back,
gradually becoming paler reddish-white to grey
towards base of tail and hips; below all white. Face
greyish-brown around muzzle and eyes, with
reddish-brown crown; fur around neck lighter,
forming reddish-blonde collar. Tail uniform blonde
or reddish-blonde. Two phenotypes have been
observed, perhaps male and female but this has
yet to be confirmed.

Small-toothed Sportive Lemur *Lepilemur microdon* EN
Lépilémur à petites dents

HB 27–32 cm, **T** 25–29 cm, **W** c. 1 kg.
Primary and secondary rainforest with dense covering of saplings and bamboo. For diurnal sleeping sites, selects large trees (over 65 cm in diameter, at human chest height).
Large species. Fur thick, above reddish-brown with dark midline stripe, below, face and sides of neck pale grey-brown to light beige, sometimes with yellowish tinge on belly; forelimbs and shoulders rich chestnut-brown; tail darkens towards tip. Eyes pale yellow; molars notably small.

Ambodimahabibo Sportive Lemur *Lepilemur otto* EN
Lépilémur d'Otto

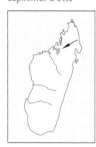

HB 28·7–30 cm, **T** 24·8–27·4 cm, **W** 853–872 g.
Dry forest patches.
Above mostly grey-brown, including shoulders and forelimbs; below generally grey to creamy; diffuse dark line from middle of crown to middle or lower back. Face and forehead essentially grey. Tail grey-brown to deep brown, sometimes with white tip.

Anjiamangirana Sportive Lemur *Lepilemur grewcockorum* CR
Lépilémur des Grewcock

170–360 m

HB c. 25 cm, **T** 28–29 cm, **W** 900 g.
Dense primary forest fragments in mountainous and coastal areas.
Fur mainly grey above, pale grey to white below, with chocolate-mottled areas on shoulders and along sides of body; dark stripe on midline of crown may continue onto back in some individuals. Some whitish-pink above mouth, and whitish on chin and throat. Ears fairly conspicuous, with short hairs on dorsal surface, making them look almost pink. Tail usually all grey, but can have variable white tip.

Milne-Edwards's Sportive Lemur *Lepilemur edwardsi* EN
Lépilémur de Milne-Edwards

HB 26–29 cm, **T** 26–29 cm, **W** 965 g.
Tropical dry deciduous lowland forest.
One of the larger sportive lemurs. Above beige-grey with strong reddish tones and usually darker median stripe down back; shoulders, forelimbs and upper thighs more chestnut-brown; underside grey with creamy patches. Face darkish grey to brown; ears prominent. Tail reddish above, greyish below, often tipped white.

0–450 m

Sahafary Sportive Lemur *Lepilemur septentrionalis* CR
Lépilémur septentrional

HB 18–19 cm, **T** c. 25 cm, **W** 600–750 g.
Tropical dry deciduous and gallery forest fragments. Small. Pale greyish-brown above and on head, grey below; often, a dark median stripe from crown to middle of back; and occasionally brownish tinges around shoulders. Ears project beyond fur but less prominent than in most other sportive lemurs. Tail pale brown, darkening towards tip.

160–540 m

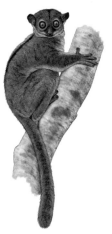

Sahamalaza Sportive Lemur *Lepilemur sahamalaza* CR
Lépilémur de Sahamalaza

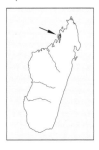

HB 19–24 cm, **T** c. 24 cm, **W** 720 g.
Primary and older secondary forest and forest patches in transitional subhumid forests of southern Sambirano, with tree heights of up to 25 m. Generally more numerous in areas with more large trees, more closed canopy, and greater abundance of food plants, suitable sleeping holes, and vegetation tangles.
Small. Fur colour variable, perhaps depending on age. Upper body mainly reddish-brown, with grey or creamy underparts, and reddish-brown to deep brown tail; diffuse dark dorsal stripe from crown to lower back. Face mainly grey, but forehead and around ears reddish-brown, sometimes with diffuse darker patches.

Tsiombikibo Sportive Lemur   *Lepilemur ahmansonorum* CR
Lépilémur des Ahmanson

10–20 m

HB 24–30 cm, **T** 23–34 cm, **W** 550 g.
Dry forest.
Mostly dark grey above and below, with diffuse reddish-brown on dorsal surface of limbs, especially towards tips; vague black stripe may be present on crown. Tail dark reddish-brown above, pale greyish-blonde below.

Gray's Sportive Lemur   *Lepilemur dorsalis* EN
Lépilémur à dos gris

100–370 m

HB 23–26 cm, **T** 26–28 cm, **W** 770 g.
Primary and secondary tropical moist lowland, gallery and montane forests that are subject to a dry season each year; also bush country and timber plantations.
Long-tailed species with blunt muzzle. Fur medium brown to grey-brown above and on tail, with indistinct, darker brown median dorsal stripe; underside lighter grey-brown, paler towards throat. Face dark grey to brown with large orange-red or brown eyes; ears small and rounded, and almost hidden in fur.

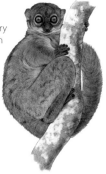

Mittermeier's Sportive Lemur   *Lepilemur mittermeieri* CR
Lépilémur de Mittermeier

HB 27·1–29·2 cm, **T** 25·4–28·1 cm, **W** c. 730 g.
Primary and secondary tropical dry deciduous forest.
Above reddish-grey, with dark brown to black mid-line stripe, occasionally extending onto top of head. Tail uniform pale reddish-grey to brown, darkening towards tip. Face mask-like and grey, with whiter markings below eyes and on chin.

Nosy Be Sportive Lemur   *Lepilemur tymerlachsoni*   `CR`
Lépilémur de Nosy Be

HB c. 23 cm, **T** c. 25 cm, **W** 840 g.
Primary and secondary tropical moist lowland forest
that is subject to a dry season each year; apparently commonest in secondary forest.
Above light brownish-grey, with diffuse pale
reddish-brown on upper half of back, foreparts of
thighs, and edges of limbs; dark brown to black
midline stripe from head to lower back; underside
pale greyish-white. Mask-like face grey. Tail uniform
light reddish-grey to brown.

10–35 m

Daraina Sportive Lemur   *Lepilemur milanoii*   `EN`
Lépilémur de Daraina

HB 22–24 cm, **T** 25–26 cm, **W** 711 g.
Primary and secondary tropical moist, gallery and dry
deciduous lowland forest.
Notably long, thick fur, generally reddish-brown
above, greyish-white below; diffuse, darker brown
midline stripe from crown partially down back.
Crown mostly reddish-brown, face grey-brown,
forming sort of mask. Limbs mainly grey, but front of
thighs reddish-brown. Tail uniform reddish-brown.

15–380 m

Ankarana Sportive Lemur   *Lepilemur ankaranensis*   `EN`
Lépilémur de l'Ankarana

HB c. 22 cm, **T** c. 27 cm, **W** 730 g.
Tropical dry lowland and moist montane forest.
Small; very similar to *L. septentrionalis*, but chromosom-
ally distinct (the two are geographically close but do
not overlap). Pale greyish-brown above, with grey
underside; often, a dark median stripe from crown
down back, and brownish tinges on shoulders. Ears
project beyond fur but less prominent than in most
other sportive lemurs. Tail pale brown, darkening
towards tip.

0–1500 m

BAMBOO, TRUE AND RUFFED LEMURS   Lemuridae

Grey Bamboo Lemur *Hapalemur griseus* VU
Hapalémur gris

Primary and secondary tropical moist lowland and montane forest, generally in dense stands of bamboo.
0–1375 m

H. g. ranomafanensis VU

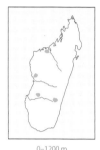

0–1200 m

HB c. 30 cm, **T** c. 37 cm, **W** c. 700–850 g. Smaller than *H. aureus*. Upperparts grey to olive-grey; face and underparts lighter. Paler grey ring around eye. Ears small and rounded. Tail grey.

H. g. griseus VU

0–1375 m

HB c. 30 cm, **T** c. 37 cm, **W** c. 700–850 g. Fur grey or olivaceous to rust-brown, usually with darker and more reddish patches on head and shoulders; face paler. Muzzle short; ears relatively large but nearly hidden in fur.

H. g. gilberti DD

1250–1360 m

HB c. 28 cm, **T** c. 35 cm, **W** c. 967 g. Bulkier than *H. g. griseus*. Dorsal fur grey-brown, throat and chest grey, belly reddish; face with dark grey ring encircling eyes. Ears shorter than in *H. g. griseus* or *H. meridionalis*. Tail dark grey.

Southern Bamboo Lemur *Hapalemur meridionalis* VU
Hapalémur méridional

0–1600 m

HB 28–30 cm, **T** 35–37 cm, **W** 840–870 g.
Subtropical moist lowland and montane forest, generally in areas of dense bamboo; also present in degraded littoral forests dominated by *Ravenala* and *Pandanus*.
Similar in size to *H. griseus*, but fur darker and redder, ears longer and tail shorter. Muzzle short; ears relatively large but nearly hidden in fur. Tail 103–113% of head–body length.

Northern Bamboo Lemur *Hapalemur occidentalis* VU
Hapalémur occidental

0–1000 m

HB 27–28 cm, **T** 36–39 cm, **W** c. 846–1200 g.
Dry deciduous forest, semi-humid transitional forest and humid forest containing stands of bamboo and areas of bamboo vines; also degraded habitats and patches of bamboo surrounded by agricultural land.
More uniform grey-brown than the smaller *H. griseus*, with paler face than congeners. Ears similar in length to those of *H. griseus*, but they protrude from fur. Female heavier than male.

Lac Alaotra Bamboo Lemur *Hapalemur alaotrensis* CR
Hapalémur de l'Alaotra

750 m

HB c. 40 cm, **T** c. 40 cm, **W** 1·2–1·3 kg.
Reedbeds and papyrus marshes.
Much larger than congeners apart from *H. aureus*; has strikingly rounded head and dense woolly pelage. Fur above grey-brown; face and underside paler grey. Crown and nape chestnut-brown. Ears relatively short and hidden in fur.

Golden Bamboo Lemur *Hapalemur aureus* CR
Hapalémur doré

625–1625 m

HB c. 34 cm, **T** c. 41 cm, **W** 1·3–1·5 kg.
Primary tropical moist mid-altitude and montane rainforest, associated with bamboo.
Largest and heaviest member of genus. Generally reddish or greyish-brown above, darker on shoulders, back, crown and tail (tail darker towards tip); below and inner sides of limbs paler golden-brown. Head rounded, with short white ears that are tipped with golden-brown hairs but not tufted. Pink nose contrasts with black muzzle, which is surrounded by ring of orange to golden-yellow fur that extends to cheeks and throat ("mutton chops"). Eyebrows golden.

Greater Bamboo Lemur *Prolemur simus* `CR`
Lémur à nez large

25–1600 m

HB 40–42 cm, **T** 45–48 cm, **W** 2·2–2·5 kg.
Humid primary and secondary rainforest associated with giant bamboo (*Cathariostachys madagascariensis*); also marshland. Sometimes degraded habitat and plantations.
Largest bamboo lemur; very distinctive. Fur above and on tail rather drab greyish-brown with slight reddish tinge; crown, neck, shoulders and upper arms more olive-brown; below, paler creamy brown; rusty-brown pygal patch. Muzzle blunt, dark grey; ears large, usually with prominent white tufts. Population on Andringitra Massif may be a distinct colour morph: head, upperparts, throat and underparts uniformly deep golden-red, and tip of tail grey; face and muzzle dark, ears large and prominent but lacking the characteristic white tufts of the species; taxonomic status of this morph requires further investigation.

Ring-tailed Lemur *Lemur catta* `EN`
Lémur catta

0–2600 m

HB 39–46 cm, **T** 56–63 cm, **W** 2·2 kg.
Varied, mainly wooded areas, including tropical dry scrub, Didiereaceae forest, brushland of spiny *Euphorbia* (with water nearby), and wet, deciduous, gallery and montane humid forest.
Unmistakable, with long, bushy black-tipped tail, ringed with black and white transverse bands along its entire length. Relatively large species. Fur above pale grey to rosy brown, with grey flanks, limbs and haunches, and darker grey on crown and neck; belly and extremities white to cream, with throat, cheeks, ears and forehead white. Muzzle greyish; nose black. Eyes of adults brilliant yellow to red, framed by triangular black rings. Scrotum naked. Population of high, relatively cool Andringitra Massif considerably darker, with denser, woollier fur and fewer dark rings on tail.

Andringitra

normal

Brown Lemur *Eulemur fulvus* `VU`
Lémur brun

0–1880 m

HB 43–50 cm, **T** 41–51 cm, **W** 1·5 kg.
Primary and secondary rainforest and dry deciduous forest.
Small to medium-sized lemur. Female slightly paler than male, but sexual dimorphism generally less obvious than in other species of *Eulemur*. Upperparts and tail brown to grey-brown; below paler, tending towards creamy tan. Face, muzzle and crown dark brown to almost black, cheeks and beard white; patches of light fur above eyes variable, strongly marked in north but barely discernible in south. Eyes orange-red.

Rufous Brown Lemur *Eulemur rufus* `VU`
Lémur roux

HB 40–48 cm, **T** 45–55 cm, **W** 1·6 kg.
Primary and secondary tropical dry lowland forest.
Medium-sized, and sexually dichromatic, similar to *E. rufifrons*. Male dark olive-grey with deep brown tinge on and above tail, lighter below; hands red; crown dark brick-red, cheek beard golden-red; muzzle black, with broad black mid-facial stripe from crown to nose; sides of nose and patches above eyes creamy white. Female gingery-red with orange underside, and short golden-red cheek beard; crown black, large grey-white cheek spots.

Red-fronted Brown Lemur *Eulemur rufifrons* `VU`
Lémur à front roux

0–1700 m

HB 40–48 cm, **T** 45–55 cm, **W** 2·1–2·5 kg.
Tropical dry lowland forest in west, and tropical moist lowland to montane forest in east.
Relatively large, sexually dichromatic species, generally similar to *E. rufus*. Male iron-grey above with greyish-fawn underside; crown dark red; tail black towards tip; digits red. Female brownish-olive-grey above with whitish-red underside; head reddish; tail tipped orange. All young born with adult male coloration; infant females change into adult coloration in 7–17 weeks.

♂

♀

White-fronted Brown Lemur *Eulemur albifrons* `VU`
Lémur à front blanc

0–1600 m

HB 39–42 cm, **T** 50–54 cm, **W** 1·9 kg.
Primary and secondary tropical moist lowland forest and montane rainforest.
Medium-sized, sexually dichromatic species with notably convex forehead. Coloration extremely variable and differs greatly between sexes. Upperparts and tail of male medium to dark brown, darkening and becoming redder towards rear; below pale grey, sometimes creamy white on throat and chest; muzzle jet-black, contrasting with thick snowy-white beard, bushy cheeks, forehead and crown; eyes reddish-orange. Female greyish-brown above and on tail, with dark grey on chest and shoulders, and paler underparts; muzzle blackish-grey, rest of head greyish. Albinism fairly common.

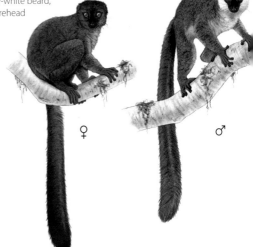

♀

♂

Sanford's Brown Lemur *Eulemur sanfordi* EN
Lémur de Sanford

0–1400 m

HB 38–40 cm, **T** 50–55 cm, **W** 1·9 kg.
Primary and secondary tropical moist, gallery and dry deciduous lowland forest, and montane forest; appears to favour secondary forest. Absent from very dry forests.
Medium-sized, sexually dichromatic species. Male above brownish-grey, darker along back and on tail; below pale brownish-grey; limbs reddish; top of head cream-coloured to brown, always paler than back; prominent ear tufts, ranging from off-white to cream to slightly rufous, complemented by long (but not bushy) cheek whiskers of similar colour, giving appearance of mane; nose, muzzle and face black. Female similar in appearance, grey-brown above and on tail, paler grey below; face, shoulders and upper back grey; often, lighter patches above eyes; lacks cheek whiskers and ear tufts.

White-collared Brown Lemur *Eulemur cinereiceps* CR
Lémur à collier blanc

0–615 m

HB 39–40 cm, **T** 50–55 cm, **W** 2 kg.
Tropical moist lowland forest.
Medium-sized, sexually dichromatic species. Male above grey-brown, often with dark brown stripe down spine; tail and lower limbs also slightly darker; underparts and much of face grey; dark grey crown becomes paler on neck and shoulders; cheeks and bushy cheek ruffs (beard) white or light cream. Female redder overall, and with reddish-brown upperparts with paler underparts; face uniform slate-grey, with short reddish-brown beard (not bushy like that of male). Female virtually indistinguishable from female *E. collaris*, whereas males readily separable on beard colour.

Red-collared Brown Lemur *Eulemur collaris* EN
Lémur à collier roux

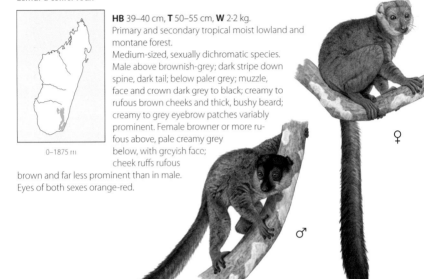

HB 39–40 cm, **T** 50–55 cm, **W** 2·2 kg.
Primary and secondary tropical moist lowland and
montane forest.
Medium-sized, sexually dichromatic species.
Male above brownish-grey; dark stripe down
spine, dark tail; below paler grey; muzzle,
face and crown dark grey to black; creamy to
rufous brown cheeks and thick, bushy beard;
creamy to grey eyebrow patches variably
prominent. Female browner or more rufous above, pale creamy grey
below, with greyish face;
cheek ruffs rufous
brown and far less prominent than in male.
Eyes of both sexes orange-red.

0–1875 m

Black Lemur *Eulemur macaco* EN
Lémur noir

HB 39–45 cm, **T** 51–65 cm, **W** 1·9–2 kg.
Primary and secondary tropical moist lowland and
montane forest. Fairly adaptable and has been
reported from dry forest, forest–agriculture mosaics
(coffee and cashew) and timber plantations.
Medium-sized, sexually dichromatic species. Male
uniform dark chocolate-brown to black with
lavish black ear tufts. Female golden-brown
to chestnut-brown above, paler on
flanks but darker on tail; below
typically creamy white on belly,
grading to cinnamon on chin,
and this coloration may
continue to just below eyes and ear tufts; muzzle and
interocular stripe grey to black,
crown darker charcoal-grey;
ears tufted with long whitish
hairs. Eyes of both sexes yellow
to brownish-orange. Young similar in
coloration to adult male.

0–1600 m

Blue-eyed Black Lemur *Eulemur flavifrons* `CR`
Lémur aux yeux turquoise

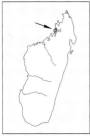

0–1200 m

HB 39–45 cm, **T** 51–65 cm, **W** 1·8–1·9 kg.
Somewhat disturbed primary and secondary subtropical subhumid forests, in transition zone between Sambirano region to north and western dry deciduous forests to south.
Medium-sized, sexually dichromatic species. Differs from *E. macaco*, with which long considered conspecific, in slightly smaller size, unique bright blue, grey or green eyes, and lack of ear tufts. Male all-black (sometimes tinged brown), with distinct ridge of fur on forehead forming crest. Female golden-orange to reddish-tan above, creamy white to grey below, with darker reddish-brown hands and feet; muzzle slate-grey, face paler, crown rufous tan.

♂

♀

Crowned Lemur *Eulemur coronatus* `EN`
Lémur couronné

0–1400 m

HB 34–36 cm, **T** 41–49 cm, **W** 1·3 kg.
Prefers semi-deciduous dry lowland and mid-altitude forest, but may be found in practically all forest types, including high-altitude tropical moist forest; also wooded grassland and agricultural areas. Inhabits all levels of the forest, but typically found in lianas and thick cover and on terminal branches; also readily descends to ground to travel, eat fallen fruit, or lick soil; sometimes seen moving delicately through knife-edged karst "tsingy". Sexually dichromatic. Male grey-brown above, becoming richer chestnut-brown on flanks and limbs, and darker on tail; below paler creamy grey; only tip of muzzle black, with face and ears pale grey to white; forward-pointing, V-shaped orange-brown crown runs from eyebrows onto cheeks; dark grey to black patch in centre of crown; eyes encircled by orange-red rings. Female grey above and on flanks, limbs, tail, top of head and cheeks; tail darkens towards tip; underparts, face and ears paler grey to creamy white; nose black, muzzle dark grey; V-shaped marking above forehead chestnut-orange, but less prominent than in male, and does not curve round to cheeks. Ears of both sexes large, white and prominent. Tail long and bushy.

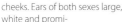

♀

♂

Red-bellied Lemur *Eulemur rubriventer* VU
Lémur à ventre roux

70–2400 m

♀

HB 35–40 cm, **T** 43–53 cm, **W** 2 kg.
Primary and secondary rainforest at middle to high elevations.
Medium-sized, sexually dichromatic species, with heavy fur and remarkably small ears that are virtually hidden in the fur. Male deep chestnut-brown to maroon-red above, with slightly lighter coppery-red underside; tail darker, shading to black; muzzle, face and rest of head black; conspicuous patches of white skin form large "tear-drops" below inner corner of each eye; no bushy beard or ear tufts as in other *Eulemur*, but fur around ears particularly dense, giving head a robust appearance. Female umber above and on tail, but throat, chest and belly contrasting yellow-white, sometimes extending to cheeks; facial coloration as in male, but white patches beneath eyes reduced; head lacks long bushy cheek hairs, thus appearing less robust. Eyes of both sexes yellow.

♂

Mongoose Lemur *Eulemur mongoz* CR
Lémur mongoz

0–400 m

♀

HB 30–35 cm, **T** 45–48 cm, **W** 1·1–1·3 kg.
Primary and secondary tropical dry deciduous forest and scrub.
Small, thickly furred species; sexes fairly similar in size and appearance. Male above grey-brown, darker at tip of tail; also a darker grey pygal patch; back of neck and shoulders often rufous brown; below paler creamy grey; muzzle grey, face greyish-white, cheeks and beard rufous; triangular bald patch on top of head sometimes results from excessive rubbing during scent-marking. Female greyer above, with pale grey muzzle and darker slate-grey forehead and face; face surrounded by bushy white beard that extends to ears and down throat onto forelimbs. Eyes reddish-orange in both sexes.

♂

Black-and-white Ruffed Lemur *Varecia variegata* `CR`
Vari noir et blanc

Primary forest at low to medium altitudes.
0–1300 m

V. v. subcincta `CR`

HB 43–57 cm, **T** 60–65 cm, **W** 3.1–3.6 kg
Coat fluffy; tail long and bushy; ears "ruffed" with long, thick white hair; distinct white belt around black back, often with some dark brown, especially on lower back. Top of head, face, belly, inner aspects of limbs, extremities and tail black; outer aspects of limbs and base of tail white. Eyes yellow to amber.

V. v. variegata `CR`

HB 43–57 cm, **T** 60–65 cm, **W** 3.1–3.6 kg
Coat fluffy; tail long and bushy; ears tufted or "ruffed", with long, thick white hair. Top of head, face, shoulders, belly, inner aspects of limbs, extremities and tail black; back, flanks, rump and most of hind limbs usually white. Distinguished from race *editorum* by thick white longitudinal band in centre of upper back. Pattern varies locally, and intermediate forms exist.

V. v. editorum `CR`

HB c. 43–57 cm, **T** c. 60–65 cm, **W** c. 3.1–3.6 kg.
Coat fluffy; tail long and bushy; ears "ruffed" with long, thick white hair. Top of head, face, upper back, belly, inner aspects of limbs, extremities and tail black; lower back, flanks, rump and outer aspects of limbs usually white.

Red Ruffed Lemur *Varecia rubra* CR
Vari roux

0–1200 m

HB 50–55 cm, **T** 60–65 cm, **W** 3–3·6 kg.
Primary and secondary tropical moist lowland forest; prefers tall forest, and often seen in crowns of large feeding trees.
Fur mainly deep wine-red (sometimes red-orange or honey-blonde) on upperparts, legs, throat, cheeks and ear tufts; underside, tail, insides of limbs, feet, face, forehead, muzzle and crown black; white patch on nape; sometimes small pale patches on muzzle, digits and heels.

WOOLLY LEMURS, SIFAKAS AND INDRI   Indriidae

0–1260 m

Eastern Woolly Lemur   *Avahi laniger* VU
Avahi laineux

HB 27·7–32·2 cm, **T** 30·4–36·6 cm, **W** 1·1–1·3 kg.
Tropical moist lowland, montane and secondary forest.
Above grey-brown to reddish, becoming paler towards rusty-red tail; underparts grey. Face brownish, with paler band or distinct patches above eyes and lighter fur on cheeks and throat. Small ears largely hidden by thick fur. Dense, short fur tightly curled on back.

Masoala Woolly Lemur   *Avahi mooreorum*   EN
Avahi des Moore

HB 28·4–33 cm, **T** 29·4–37·2 cm, **W** 920 g.
Primary rainforest.
Fur above mottled mixture of chocolate-brown and light brown, gradually lightening towards cream-coloured base of tail; below, including undersides of limbs, grey; distinct whitish patch, characteristic of the genus, on rear of each hindlimb; tail reddish-brown. Head darker than back, and facemask apparent, although not as pronounced as in other eastern *Avahi* species. No noticeable eyebrow; whitish patch under mandible. Ears not readily visible, blending into rest of head.

Peyriéras's Woolly Lemur   *Avahi peyrierasi* VU
Avahi de Peyriéras

HB 26–31·7 cm, **T** 28·5–34·4 cm, **W** 1–1·1 kg.
Primary tropical moist lowland and montane forest; also secondary and disturbed forest but seems to prefer intact primary forest with tall trees.
Slightly smaller than very similar *A. laniger*. Above grey-brown, with grey or white underside and red-brown tail. Outsides of thighs grey-brown, insides white; small white bands along interior of legs and sometimes on upperparts. In some individuals, face completely encircled by white border, including white beard and cheeks.

73

Betsileo Woolly Lemur *Avahi betsileo* EN
Avahi du Betsileo

HB 26–31 cm, **T** 28·3–34·4 cm, **W** 1–1·2 kg.
Primary tropical rainforest.
Differs from other eastern woolly lemurs in mainly light reddish-brown upperparts and on outside of limbs; underside dark grey towards midline, diffusing to pale grey ventrolaterally. Tail mainly reddish-brown above, reddish-blonde below. Distinct facial mask, with greyish below mandible and diffuse creamy eyebrow markings. Fur thicker on head than in other eastern species of *Avahi*, giving more rounded appearance.

Manombo Woolly Lemur *Avahi ramanantsoavani* VU
Avahi de Manombo

HB 24–31 cm, **T** 33–40 cm, **W** 900–1000 g.
Primary tropical rainforest.
Slightly smaller than *A. peyrierasi*. Above grey-brown, below grey. Tail red-brown.

Southern Woolly Lemur *Avahi meridionalis* EN
Avahi méridional

HB 23–29 cm, **T** 30–33 cm, **W** 1–1·1 kg.
Primary tropical rainforest and coastal forest.
Similar in size to *A. peyrierasi*. Above grey-brown, becoming greyer on lower back and hindlimbs; below grey. Tail red-brown, becoming darker towards tip.

Western Woolly Lemur *Avahi occidentalis* VU
Avahi occidental

HB 26·9–30·3 cm, **T** 30·7–37·7 cm, **W** 830–1000 g.
Primary and secondary tropical dry deciduous forest.
One of the smallest woolly lemurs. Dense, tightly curled fur of back is pale to medium grey, sometimes flecked with brown or olive, becoming paler towards rear; tail normally grey too, but sometimes reddish. Face, throat and cheeks pale; triangular downward extension of crown into facial area.

Bemaraha Woolly Lemur *Avahi cleesei* CR
Avahi de Cleese

25–85 m

HB 23–31 cm, **T** 32–36 cm, **W** 830–980 g.
Subhumid, dry deciduous forest close to western Tsingy precipices, in larger gorges, and along small seasonal rivulets and seasonal swamps; appears to do well in disturbed habitats.
Fur above woolly and mainly brown-grey; below thin and light grey. Tail brown-grey to beige, near base slightly redder above. Characteristic white patches on outsides of hindlimbs. Snout black and hairless, fur at corners of mouth whitish; face slightly paler than blackish forehead and crown; triangular upward extension of facial area onto crown; fur of forehead immediately above face blackish, forming dark chevron. Eyes maroon, with hairless black eyelids.

Sambirano Woolly Lemur *Avahi unicolor* CR
Avahi unicolore

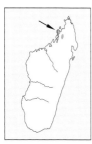

0–700 m

HB 23–31 cm, **T** 26·5–30·3 cm, **W** 830–920 g.
Tropical moist lowland forest.
One of the smallest woolly lemurs. Fur above woolly and sandy brownish-grey; tail darker grey-brown or more reddish-brown, but base normally lighter, sometimes cream-coloured; triangular beige to cream-coloured pygal patch; lighter grey underparts have thinner fur. Face only slightly paler than head and back; short, straight hair suggests facial ring or mask; snout hairless and black, fur at corners of mouth whitish. Eyes maroon.

Verreaux's Sifaka *Propithecus verreauxi* CR
Sifaka de Verreaux

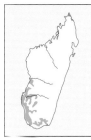

0–1300 m

HB 40–48 cm, **T** 50–60 cm, **W** 2·9 kg.
Typically tropical dry lowland and montane forests; also semi-arid spiny bush, brush-and-scrub thickets, deciduous gallery forest, riparian forest and humid forests at low elevations.
Small *Propithecus*. Fur long and thick, mainly lustrous white, often with silvery or golden tint on back and flanks; contrasts sharply with black face, muzzle, and soles of hands and feet, and also with dark reddish-brown, chocolate-brown or black crown, extending down nape; underside sparsely furred, exposing dark skin of belly and giving greyish appearance; snout deep and narrow, ears slightly tufted white. Male has reddish-brown patch on upper chest, associated with sternal gland at base of throat. Juvenile all-white except dark brown spot on crown and occasionally rufous wash on underside. A variant is also mainly white, including cheeks, ears and forehead, but with chocolate-brown cap and brownish to brownish-black on chest, back, inside of limbs, and tail (except white tip); almost always found in groups of normally coloured individuals. Other variants may have maroon patches on back, belly or limbs.

variants

Decken's Sifaka *Propithecus deckenii* CR
Sifaka de Decken

0–1250 m

HB 42–48 cm, **T** 50–60 cm, **W** 2·6–2·9 kg.
Dry deciduous forest patches; seems fairly
resilient to habitat degradation, and even
seen in *Eucalyptus* trees in middle of town of
Soalala.
Small *Propithecus*. Fur above creamy white,
often with faded silvery, golden or pale
brown tints on neck, shoulders, back and
limbs; some individuals have dark areas
on head and chest. Face naked and
black, usually with patch of white fur
across it. Bony pockets on either side of
muzzle give rather blunt-nosed appearance.

Crowned Sifaka *Propithecus coronatus* CR
Sifaka couronné

0–700 m

HB 39–45 cm, **T** 48–57 cm, **W** 3·2–3·7 kg.
Tropical dry deciduous lowland forests; occasionally
enters mangroves.
Medium-sized *Propithecus*. Fur, including
hindlimbs and tail, creamy white and variably
tinted golden-yellow to golden-brown on
upper chest, shoulders and upper forelimbs; contrasts strongly with chocolate-
brown to black crown, forehead, cheeks,
neck and throat. Muzzle blunt and rounded,
even bulbous, in form, readily distinguish-
ing it from all other sifakas. Face naked
and black, sometimes with patch of
white fur across bridge of nose and very often slight white
tufting around ears.

Coquerel's Sifaka *Propithecus coquereli* `CR`
Sifaka de Coquerel

0–300 m

HB 42–50 cm, **T** 50–60 cm, **W** 3·7 kg.
Mixed deciduous dry and semi-evergreen lowland forests, and brush-and-scrub and secondary forest immediately adjacent to primary forest; also coastal mangroves. Medium-sized *Propithecus*. Long dense fur, above mostly white, including head and tail, with prominent chestnut-brown to maroon patches covering chest, and front and inside of all limbs; also occasionally similar-coloured or even silvery patches at base of back. Skin of long, narrow muzzle and face bare and black, except for white patch of fur across bridge of nose. Ears small, black and naked; visible above white fur of head. Eyes yellow. Aberrant population has charcoal grey-black replacing reddish-brown, and dark grey on forehead.

Tattersall's Sifaka *Propithecus tattersalli* `CR`
Sifaka de Tattersall

50–700 m

HB 45–47 cm, **T** 42–47 cm, **W** 3·4–3·6 kg.
Primary dry deciduous, gallery and semi-evergreen forest patches; also coastal/littoral forest. Medium-sized species. Fur notably short and sparse, mainly creamy white above and on shoulders, upper arms and genital region, with golden-orange wash on chest and rump; forearms and tops of legs often pale orange. Crown bright golden-orange, often extending to shoulders and separated from bare black skin of face by white ruff. Ears black and prominent, with distinctive white tufts, making head appear somewhat triangular. Eyes yellow-orange.

Diademed Sifaka *Propithecus diadema* `CR`
Sifaka à diadème

200–1600 m
(above 800 m preferred)

HB 50–55 cm, **T** 44–50 cm, **W** 5·7–6·8 kg.
Primary highland rainforest; appears to require intact forest, but can be found in small forest fragments.
Largest sifaka; unmistakable, with colourful pattern, characteristic long, silky fur and prominent "diadem" fringe across forehead. Fur of shoulders and upper back slate-grey, lower back silver-grey; below white to pale grey. Forehead, cheeks and throat white with silvery or golden tints; crown black, sometimes extending to nape; blackish on chest. Arms and legs orange to yellow-gold, hands and feet black, flanks and tail pale grey to white (often with golden-white base to tail). Head is notably small and narrow; muzzle short; bare face dark grey to black; eyes reddish-brown. Male has large reddish-brown cutaneous gland in middle of throat, and perianal patch of similar colour. Juvenile paler, with yellower frontal band and lighter yellow limbs.

Milne-Edwards's Sifaka *Propithecus edwardsi* `EN`
Sifaka de Milne-Edwards

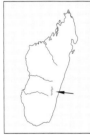

600–1600 m

HB 42–52 cm, **T** 41–48 cm, **W** 5·5 kg.
Primary and slightly degraded secondary rainforest.
Large and heavily built. Fur above dense and dark, varying from chocolate-brown to almost jet-black on head, upper body, limbs and tail; lateral whitish patches of varying extent grade into darker surrounding fur on back and flanks, sometimes meeting along spine; below equally dark, sometimes paler around upper part of chest, but less dense than dorsal coat. Face and ears bare, dark grey to black, with ears barely discernible above dark fur of head. Eyes orange-red. Juvenile resembles adults.

Silky Sifaka *Propithecus candidus* CR
Sifaka soyeux

230–1900 m

HB 48–54 cm, **T** 45–51 cm, **W** 5–6 kg.
Undisturbed primary montane rainforest; also sclerophyllous forest and even low ericoid bush.
Large white sifaka, with long, silky fur. Above mainly creamy white, sometimes with silvery-grey tints on crown, back and limbs; usually, a patch of rust-red or yellow fur at base of tail. Muzzle and face bare and normally slaty-grey-black (often with pinkish mottling around mouth), but sometimes all-pink or all-black; tips of naked black or pink ears protrude just beyond white fur of head; eyes deep orange-red. Male differs from female in having large brown patch on upper chest, resulting from scent-marking with sternal-gular gland; as breeding progresses, patch can expand onto belly. In Marojejy Massif, some individuals have all-pink face and dark fur across upper back and shoulders.

Perrier's Sifaka *Propithecus perrieri* CR
Sifaka de Perrier

0–500 m

HB 43–47 cm, **T** 42–45 cm, **W** 4·4–4·5 kg.
Tropical dry deciduous and semi-humid lowland forest; commonest in semi-evergreen forest on sandstone.
Medium-sized, with relatively short tail. Fur above long, dense and silky, deep lustrous black; below shorter, with rosy-brownish tinted chest and belly. Face bare and black; eyes dark reddish-brown. Ears naked in some individuals, furred in others; largely concealed in fur.

Indri *Indri indri* CR
Indri

HB 64–72 cm, **T** c. 5 cm, **W** 5·8–9 kg.
Primary and secondary tropical moist lowland and montane forest; also some disturbed habitats. Often found in mountainous habitats or steep terrain with ridges and valleys; uses all levels of canopy, but tends to stay in lower levels in Oct–Dec to avoid biting insects. Largest living lemur. Long, silky fur above, shorter below, skin black. Head rounded, with prominent, almost naked muzzle; large, modestly tufted, prominent ears always black. Relatively large staring eyes yellowish-green, directed forwards; long eyelashes. Coat coloration varies regionally from mainly black, with white or greyish-white patches on crown, neck, flanks, forelimbs or thighs to variegated black and white; with white typically on hindcrown, broad collar up beyond ears, and outer surfaces of legs and lower arms; heels and flanks may be tinged red or gold. Mainly black in north, generally paler further south. Melanistic and albino individuals also recorded.

0–1800 m

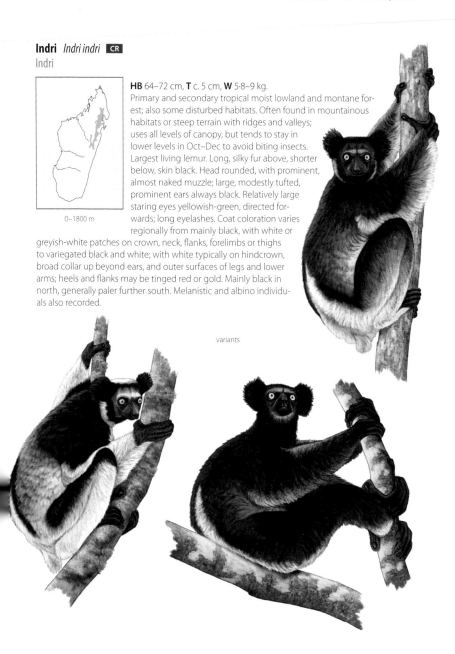

variants

Aye-aye *Daubentonia madagascariensis* EN
Aye-aye

0–1875 m

HB 30–37 cm, **T** 44–53 cm, **W** 2·4–2·6 kg).

Primary eastern rainforest, deciduous and littoral forest, mature and degraded secondary forest, cultivated areas including plantations (e.g. sugarcane, coconuts, cloves), mangrove swamps and dry scrub forest.

Unmistakable due to large size, prominent ears, long thin fingers and toes and long bushy tail; overall appearance dark greyish-brown. Above and outsides of limbs with long, coarse layer of blackish-brown, white-tipped guard hairs, giving shaggy appearance; tail dark; underparts similar to upperparts, but less dense and whiter on chest, throat and face. Head short, large and oval, with short, tapering, thinly-haired muzzle and prominent eyes that face forwards; nose pink and rather pointed; enormous, highly mobile ears naked and black. Hands and feet black with elongated digits; third digit of hand very slender, appearing withered.

POUCHED RATS, CLIMBING MICE AND FAT MICE   Nesomyidae

White-tailed Tree Rat *Brachytarsomys albicauda* LC
Antsangy à queue blanche

875–1875 m

HB 223–235 mm, **T** 220–245 mm, **W** 235–280 g.
Eastern humid lowland to montane forest.
Muzzle short; fur soft and somewhat shaggy, with dense woolly texture. Above greyish-brown, redder towards sides and head (sometimes extending onto back); belly and legs cream. Ears short. Legs, digits and toes short. Tail with scattered hairs; distal portion black, and last 8–10 mm white.

Hairy-tailed Tree Rat *Brachytarsomys villosa* VU
Antsangy à queue touffue

1200–2030 m

HB 228–245 mm, **T** 260–272 mm, **W** 236–350 g.
Eastern humid montane forest.
Muzzle short; fur soft, with woolly texture. Above greyish-brown, merging into light grey or cream on flanks and belly; some red on flanks, sometimes extending onto back. Ears short. Legs, digits and toes short; feet beige. Tail with relatively dense hair, prehensile; distal portion black, and last 8–10 mm white.

Robert's Forest Rat *Gymnuromys roberti* LC
Voalavoanala

500–1625 m

HB 156–172 mm, **T** 149–199 mm, **W** 98–128 g.
Eastern humid lowland and montane forest.
Fur dense and short; grey mottled white above, becoming grey to cream below.
Ears round and very prominent. Hindlegs large. Tail largely naked; bicoloured, dark two-tone grey above, white to pale grey below; distal portion with short, sparse white fur.

Northern Naked-tail Forest Mouse *Voalavo gymnocaudus* LC
Voalavo à queue nue

1225–1950 m

HB 80–90 mm, **T** 120–129 mm, **W** 17–25·5 g.
Eastern humid montane forest.
Fur soft and relatively thick, with silky texture; above medium grey, flanks and neck brownish; below off-white, mixed with light grey. Legs brownish-grey, feet and toes all-white. Tail largely naked and bicoloured, grey above, white below.

Eastern White-tailed Mountain Mouse *Voalavo antsahabensis* EN
Voalavo d'Antsahabe

1250–1425 m

HB 85–100 mm, **T** 102–123 mm, **W** 19–26 g.
Eastern humid montane forest.
Fur soft and relatively thick, with silky texture; above medium grey, flanks and neck brownish; below off-white mixed with light grey. Legs brownish-grey, feet and toes all-white. Largely naked tail bicoloured, grey above, white below.

Grandidier's Tufted-tail Rat *Eliurus grandidieri* LC
Rat-loir de Grandidier

410–2050 m

HB 111–164 mm, **T** 144–176 mm, **W** 42–62 g.
Eastern humid montane and sclerophyllous forest.
Above blackish-brown to blackish-grey, with flanks appearing brown or blackish-grey; below greyish-white. Muzzle proportionately more elongated than in congeners. Ears relatively long. Legs grey, feet and toes white. Tail bicoloured, grey above, pale below; distal third covered in sparse white fur, becoming thicker and longer towards tip.

Rock-loving Tufted-tail Rat *Eliurus tsingimbato* NE
Rat-loir des tsingys

100–320 m

HB 140–160 mm, **T** 140–195 mm, **W** 45·5–125 g.
Dry deciduous forest with dense understorey in limestone areas, with or without pinnacles of limestone ("tsingy").
Above dark brown to blackish-grey, merging to bright tawny on central flanks and pale tawny on hips; sharply demarcated from creamy white to bright white underside. Tops of hindfeet pale brown, becoming creamy or white on toes. Tail sparsely haired at base, becoming thicker and longer towards tip and ending in tuft (sometimes subterminally white).

Ellerman's Tufted-tail Rat *Eliurus ellermani* DD
Rat-loir d'Ellerman

400–850 m

HB 152 mm, **T** 177 mm, **W** c. 100 g.
Eastern humid lowland forest.
Above dark greyish-brown, below off-white. Distal third of tail covered with dark hair that becomes progressively thicker towards tip.

Tanala Tufted-tail Rat *Eliurus tanala* LC
Rat-loir tanala

400–1875 m

HB 140–159 mm, **T** 152–194 mm, **W** 66–97·5 g.
Eastern humid lowland, montane and sclerophyllous forest.
Above dark greyish-brown to dark brown; separated by distinct line along flanks from entirely white underside (sometimes spotted grey). Legs grey, feet and toes all-white. Distal half of tail covered in short black hairs that become progressively thicker and then white, forming distinct terminal tuft.

85

Western Tufted-tail Rat *Eliurus myoxinus* LC
Rat-loir de Milne-Edwards

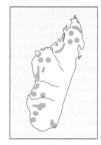

HB 117–136 mm, **T** 125–167 mm, **W** 51–75 g.
Dry deciduous and spiny bush formations in west; humid forest in east.
Above greyish-brown, separated by clear line along flanks from off-white underparts. Ears proportionally small compared with most other *Eliurus*. Legs grey, feet and toes white. Distal half of tail black or dark brown, hairs becoming denser and longer towards tip, often forming distinct brush.

0–1250 m

Lesser Tufted-tail Rat *Eliurus minor* LC
Petit Rat-loir

HB 101–124 mm, **T** 119–137 mm, **W** 21·5–49·5 g.
Humid lowland and montane forest, including disturbed and degraded forest.
Smallest *Eliurus*. Above generally brownish-grey; below beige-cream, blended with grey. Ears proportionally shorter than in most congeners. Legs grey, feet and toes all-white. Distal half of tail with dark brown to blackish hairs, becoming denser and longer towards tip.

0–2030 m

Webb's Tufted-tail Rat *Eliurus webbi* LC
Rat-loir de Webb

HB 140–159 mm, **T** 161–186 mm, **W** 66–97·5 g.
Humid lowland (including littoral) and montane forest; also degraded forest mixed with introduced trees. Prefers lowlands, becoming increasingly scarce with greater altitude.
Above generally dark brown, blackish-brown towards middle of back; belly pale grey to off-white, with brown tint on sides. Ears proportionally smaller than in other *Eliurus*. Legs grey, feet and toes all-white. Distal third of tail with dark brown hairs that become progressively thicker towards tip, forming thin tuft.

0–1450 m

Petter's Tufted-tail Rat *Eliurus petteri* EN
Rat-loir de Petter

HB 133 mm, **T** 191 mm, **W** 74 g.
Eastern humid lowland and montane forest.
Above greyish-brown, below crisp white; easily recognizable from adults of other *Eliurus* by this distinct colour contrast. Legs grey, feet and toes all-white. Distal quarter of tail covered in sparse greyish-brown hair, forming small (sometimes white) terminal tuft.

430–1200 m

Tsingy Tufted-tail Rat *Eliurus antsingy* DD
Rat-loir d'Antsingy

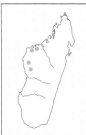

HB 142–153 mm, **T** 153–195 mm, **W** 87–101 g.
Dry deciduous forest, in karst areas forming "tsingy" (limestone towers).
Above generally drab dark brown or grey-brown, with undercoat fur nearly black; below often entirely white, sometimes mottled grey-white. Legs, feet and toes white. Distal half of tail with brown or greyish-brown hair, sometimes mixed with white hairs; ends in well-defined tuft, sometimes with consecutive white and brown whorls.

100–430 m

Carleton's Tufted-tail Rat *Eliurus carletoni* LC
Rat-loir de Carleton

HB 143–150 mm, **T** 164–183 mm, **W** 88–89 g.
Dry deciduous forest in karst areas forming "tsingy" (limestone pinnacles), or on sandy substrates.
Above typically dark brown, with forehead and face sometimes light brown; below all-white or greyish-white, with relatively well-marked division between upperparts and underparts. Legs, feet and toes white. Distal half of tail with scattered blackish-brown hairs, becoming progressively thicker towards tip; terminal tuft sometimes white or composed of whorled bands alternating white and blackish-brown.

50–835 m

Major's Tufted-tail Rat *Eliurus majori* LC
Rat-loir de Major

HB 138–164 mm, **T** 150–192 mm, **W** 56·5–93 g.
Humid lowland, montane and sclerophyllous forests.
Fur silkier and woollier than in most congeners.
Above palish to dark blackish-grey; below pale grey.
Legs grey, broad feet and toes white. Distal quarter of tail covered in sparse black hairs that become progressively thicker towards tip; sometimes, a terminal white tuft.

875–2400 m

White-tipped Tufted-tail Rat *Eliurus penicillatus* EN
Rat-loir à queue blanche

HB 145 mm, **T** 169 mm, **W** 70 g.
Eastern humid montane forest.
Above generally brownish-grey to blackish-grey; below light grey; line along flanks separating these two parts not very obvious. Legs grey, feet and toes white. Distal half of tail covered with scattered white hairs that become progressively denser towards tip.

1100–1670 m

Daniel's Tufted-tail Rat *Eliurus danieli* LC
Rat-loir de Daniel

HB 150–152 mm, **T** 179–195 mm, **W** 91–100 g.
Sandstone canyons with transitional western dry and eastern humid forest vegetation, or gallery forest; not strictly forest-dependent; and occasionally seen outside but near natural forest.
Distinctive, with contrast of grey above and greyish-white below; flanks brownish. Relatively long ears for *Eliurus*. Legs brown, feet and toes white. Tail covered with black hairs along its distal half; c. 12–15 mm from tip, these hairs become progressively longer, and white.

600–700 m

Western Big-footed Mouse *Macrotarsomys bastardi* LC
Kelibotra de Bastard

0–915 m

HB 89–103 mm,
T 120–145 mm,
W 20–26 g.
Dry deciduous for-
est and spiny bush
in areas with sandy soils.
Fur distinctly soft and fine; above greyish-brown and slightly dull
yellow; separated on flanks by distinct line from uniform white underparts.
Eyes proportionately large; snout slightly pointed; ears distinctly elongated.
Hindlegs elongated. Tail remarkably long, brownish-grey above, light grey
below; tip trimmed with a few brown hairs.

Petter's Big-footed Mouse *Macrotarsomys petteri* DD
Kelibotra de Petter

80 m

HB 160 mm,
T 238 mm, **W** 105 g.
Known from single
site, in transitional
dry deciduous forest
on red sandy soil; area sur-
rounded by spiny bush and succulent *Euphorbia*.
Above dark greyish-brown; separated by distinct line on flanks from
uniform white underparts. Eyes proportionately large; ears distinctly
elongated. Hindlegs elongated. Tail remarkably long and two-tone, dark
brown above, slightly paler below; tip covered with elongated off-white
hair tuft.

Long-tailed Big-footed Mouse *Macrotarsomys ingens* EN
Kelibotra d'Ankarafantsika

100–400 m

HB 112–150 mm, **T** 183–
240 mm, **W** 42–74 g.
Dry deciduous forest
with sandy soil.
Similar to *M. bastardi* but larger,
with relatively smaller ears. Fur fairly soft and fine; light
greyish-brown above; separated by distinct line on flanks from
uniform white underparts. Eyes proportionately large; ears distinctly
elongated. Hindlegs elongated. Tail remarkably long, brown above,
pale grey below; tip trimmed with tuft of brown hairs.

Koopman's Mountain-dwelling Mouse *Monticolomys koopmani* `LC`
Voalavo de Koopman

900–2030 m

HB 94–101 mm, **T** 134–143 mm, **W** 25–27 g.
Eastern humid lowland and montane forest.
Fur relatively thick, soft and fine; brownish-grey above, lighter grey below. Ears fairly short. Legs relatively long, with creamy white fur; feet and toes flesh-pink. Tail with sparse blackish fur at base; hairs progressively more numerous towards tip, and sometimes with some white; no obvious tail tuft.

Malagasy Giant Jumping Rat *Hypogeomys antimena* `EN`
Vositse géant

40 –100 m

HB 305–345 mm, **T** 215–240 mm, **W** 1·1–1·3 kg.
Dry deciduous forest on sandy substrate.
Largest extant rodent in Madagascar. Upperparts with relatively stiff hairs, brownish-grey to reddish-brown; head fur slightly darker, underparts light brown; subadult distinctly greyer than adult. Ears long (60 mm) and pointed. Forelimbs distinctly less developed than long, plantigrade hindfeet.

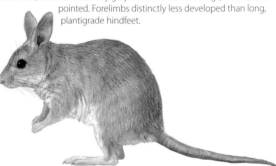

Lesser Short-tailed Rat *Brachyuromys betsileoensis* LC
Petit Ramirohitra

900–2450 m

HB 140–184 mm, **T** 77–95 mm, **W** 96–140 g.
Eastern humid montane and sclerophyllous forest; also degraded forest, agricultural areas (e.g. abandoned rice paddies) and different types of marshland. Swims in open, relatively deep water.
Muzzle short. Fur soft, dense and relatively short; above greyish-brown with some rufous; greyish-beige below. Ears short, velvety toward tips, and largely hairless toward bases. Legs short, feet relatively large. Tail above black, below distinctly paler, with sparse fine metallic grey fur.

Greater Short-tailed Rat *Brachyuromys ramirohitra* LC
Grand Ramirohitra

1210–1960 m

HB 140–165 mm, **T** 84–110 mm, **W** 64–117 g.
Eastern humid lowland to montane forest.
Muzzle short. Fur soft, dense and relatively short; above greyish-brown, with some rufous; greyish-beige below.
Ears short, velvety toward tips, and largely hairless toward bases. Legs short, feet relatively large. Tail above black, below distinctly paler, with sparse fine metallic grey fur.

Eastern Red Forest Rat *Nesomys rufus* LC
Nésomys roux

650–2000 m
(mostly above 1900 m)

HB 170–200 mm, **T** 160–180 mm, **W** 135–185 g.
Eastern humid lowland and montane forest.
Above reddish-brown, often with black hair admixed, especially in middle of back; more saturated with red along flanks; below rusty red, with some off-white, especially along midline. Ears moderately long. Legs, feet and toes dark brown. Tail with short, sparse black hairs around base, becoming progressively slightly longer towards tip; distal 8–20 mm white.

Lowland Red Forest Rat *Nesomys audeberti* LC
Nésomys d'Audebert

0–1050 m

HB 195–203 mm, **T** 169–173 mm, **W** 193–239 g.
Eastern humid lowland and montane forest.
Above reddish-brown, often with black hair admixed, especially in middle of back; below largely rusty-red, with central portion and throat white. Snout elongated; ears moderately long. Legs, feet and toes with dark brown fur. Base of tail has short black hairs that become progressively longer and denser towards tip, which can be white.

Tsingy Red Forest Rat *Nesomys lambertoni* EN
Nésomys de Lamberton

c. 100 m

HB 189–195 mm, **T** 183–191 mm, **W** 225–243 g.
Dry deciduous forest in karst areas forming "tsingy" (limestone pinnacle) habitat. Makes its dens in small caves and rock shelters in limestone.
Large, and squirrel-like from distance. Above dark reddish-brown, with black hair admixed, especially in middle of back; more saturated with red along flanks; below light brown. Elongated snout; long ears. Legs dark brown to black. Tail completely covered in long, thick dark brown hair.

OLD WORLD FRUIT BATS Pteropodidae

Madagascar Rousette *Rousettus madagascariensis* VU
Roussette de Madagascar

FA 66–80 mm, **W** 31–81·5 g.
Eastern humid forests, western and north-western dry deciduous forests; also plantations and other agricultural areas, and villages.
Fur overall brown, with reddish-brown and greyish tones; paler below, and sparser on neck, shoulders and throat; hairs of dorsal fur greyish to brownish at bases and darker brown at tips. Uropatagium sparsely furred; dorsal side of tibia practically naked; wings attach between first and second toes. Postorbital width usually greater than interorbital width; supraoccipital crest low, zygomatic arches slender.

0–1150 m

Madagascar Straw-coloured Fruit Bat *Eidolon dupreanum* VU
Roussette-paillée de Madagascar

FA 117·5–134 mm, **W** 285–300 g.
Humid, dry deciduous and spiny forests; rare or absent in forests without rocky outcrops for roosting; survives in highly modified landscapes with minimal native vegetation.
Fur short; brownish-straw above, with bright orange-brown to deep tawny collar (more prominent in male); tawny olive below. Muzzle elongated and nearly hairless; rhinarium prominent, nostrils flush with long slender snout. Eyes large; irides raw umber. Ears elongated ovals; hairless behind, with fur at bases. Face mostly hairless, with some short, soft dark brown hairs around eyes and onto snout. Fur extends over upper arm and slightly onto forearm and upper surface of legs and uropatagium but not onto wing membrane. Uropatagium split, extending partially off each leg; calcar short and slightly haired dorsally. Tail short, with 2–2·5 vertebrae protruding. Wings long, pointed and fairly narrow, blackish-brown; membranes extend from sides of dorsum and back of first toe; at rest, ends of wings are folded back, with tips folded in.

10–1200 m

Madagascar Flying Fox *Pteropus rufus* VU
Roussette marron

FA 154–173 mm, **W** 500–750 g.
Humid and dry deciduous forests. Mainly roosts in lowlands.
Back and flanks dark brown, mantle buff, orange-buff or yellowish-buff, contrasting with rump; below buff, orange-buff or yellowish-brown, darker in anal region. Muzzle, face, cheeks and area around eyes medium brown, with contrasting yellowish-buff crown and area between eyes. Eyes large, with brown irides. Ears long, naked, exposed and attenuated at tips, and sub-acutely pointed. Fur extends one-third or half-way down forearm, and onto wing membrane; tibia naked or very thinly haired above. Uropatagium well developed in centre (c. 15 mm in depth), usually wholly covered by overhanging hairs of rump.

0–1200 m

TRIDENT BATS Rhinonycteridae

Rufous Trident Bat *Triaenops menamena* LC
Triaenops roux

0–550 m
(exceptionally to 1450 m)

FA 46–56 mm, **W** 6–16 g.
Areas of limestone karst, in dry deciduous lowland forest, dry open palm savanna, and spiny bush; also dry vegetation on sand (original, transitional or degraded dry deciduous forest), and locally other forest types (e.g. gallery forest). Colour varies from bright orange or reddish-orange to brownish, pale brown or dark greyish-brown, usually similar above and below; hairs darker around eyes. Ears and noseleaf pale pinkish and pale grey to dark greyish-brown; wing membranes dark brown. Noseleaf large and rounded or pentagonal, with strap-like longitudinal projection resembling hourglass across anterior part of anterior leaf, above deep anterior medial emargination; posterior leaf has three tall, pointed projections at rear, and long lanceolated projection with sharply pointed tip at front; two lateral leaflets. Ears short, wide and pointed, with prominent step-like emargination on anterior margin.

Golden Trident Bat *Paratriaenops auritus* VU
Triaenops de Grandidier

0–600 m

FA 43–51 mm, **W** 5–8 g.
Lowland dry deciduous forest combined with limestone karst.
Golden reddish to orange or bright brown, darker above than below. Ears and noseleaf pale greyish; wing membranes dark brown. Noseleaf large, narrow and rounded, with strap-like longitudinal, and deeply bifurcated projection across anterior part of anterior leaf, above deep anterior medial emargination; posterior leaf has three tall, pointed projections (not emarginated at bases) on posterior part, and short, laterally flattened, slightly upward-directed projection on anterior part; no lateral leaflets, but thickened ridge beneath margin of anterior noseleaf. Ears large and pointed, with anterior margin evenly rounded.

Trouessart's Trident Bat *Paratriaenops furcula* LC
Triaenops de Trouessart

0–140 m

FA 42–49 mm, **W** 3–9 g.
Areas of limestone karst, in dry deciduous lowland forest, dry open palm savanna, and spiny bush; also dry vegetation on sand (original, transitional or degraded dry deciduous forest, and spiny bush), and locally other forest types (e.g. gallery forest).
Grey, greyish-brown, dull brown or occasionally pale yellowish-grey, darker above than below. Ears and noseleaf pale grey or greyish-brown; wing membranes dark brown. Noseleaf large, narrow and rounded, with strap-like, longitudinal and deeply bifurcated projection across anterior part of anterior leaf, above deep anterior medial emargination; posterior leaf has three tall, pointed projections (not emarginated at bases) on posterior part, and short, laterally flattened, slightly upward-directed projection on anterior part; no lateral leaflets, but thickened ridge beneath margin of anterior noseleaf. Ears large and pointed, with anterior margin evenly rounded.

OLD WORLD LEAF-NOSED BATS Hipposideridae

Commerson's Leaf-nosed Bat *Macronycteris commersonii* NT
Phyllorhine de Commerson

0–1350 m

FA 80–103 mm, **W** 39·5–98 g.
Variety of forested and wooded habitats, including degraded forest and ecotone between forest and agricultural landscapes. Fur dense and short, reddish-brown to dark brown above, somewhat paler below; flanks and armpits white; dark band across shoulders. Ears long and narrow; frontal sac present in both sexes. Distinctive noseleaf divided into four cells on posterior margin, with three or four lateral leaflets. Slightly larger than *M. cryptovalorona*, but difficult to distinguish.

Madagascar Cryptic Leaf-nosed Bat *Macronycteris cryptovalorona* NE
Phyllorhine cryptique

FA 80–81 mm, **W** 26–42·5 g.
Dry deciduous forest and spiny bush.
Fur dense and short, reddish-brown to dark brown above, somewhat paler below; armpits white. Ears long and narrow. Distinctive noseleaf divided into four cells on posterior margin, with four lateral leaflets. Slightly smaller than *M. commersonii*, but difficult to distinguish.

95

SHEATH-TAILED BATS Emballonuridae

Mauritian Tomb Bat *Taphozous mauritianus* `LC`
Taphien de Maurice

0–900 m

FA 58–65 mm, **W** 20–36 g.
Open woodland and grassland with more than 500 mm of rain per year; also gallery forest and swamps along large rivers. Often found in anthropogenic habitats (e.g. roosting under eaves of houses). Fur sleek and close to body; dark above, appearing grizzled due to tricoloured hair, whitish at tip, grey-brown in middle, and pale brown at base; white below. Ear triangular; tragus oval, as broad as long; long, thin postorbital processes of skull taper and curve down around eye sockets; rounded braincase rises above plane of face, resulting in curved profile with little or no sagittal crest; deep, saucer-like depression in frontal area. Adult male with conspicuous gular pouch; radio-metacarpal sacs on wings.
Long, narrow wings make manoeuvring in tight spaces difficult; wingtip folding facilitates efficient crawling on roost substrates. Posterior margin of uropatagium supported on each side by strong calcar; tail projects through middle of this membrane, which is furred up to this point.

Rock-dwelling Sheath-tailed Bat *Paremballonura tiavato* `LC`
Emballonure des rochers

0–350 m

FA 35–41 mm, **W** 2·7–3·8 g.
Lowland dry forest in karst areas.
Fur long, shaggy and silky; above uniform pale to medium greyish-brown; below paler buff-brown, with greyish-brown cast. Ear long (11–15 mm), terminating in slightly pointed tip; inner part of tragus convex, with hatchet-shaped sharp anterior projection. Calcar shorter than tibia.

Peters's Sheath-tailed Bat *Paremballonura atrata* LC
Emballonure de Madagascar

0–900 m

FA 37–41 mm, **W** 5–7·1 g.
Humid rainforest and nearby.
Above uniform dark slate-grey to black; below slightly paler. Snout rather pointed, and extends well beyond lower lip. Ears broad, rounded and prominent, with distinct indentation near tip; inner surface of pinna heavily ribbed; tragus longer than broad, with smooth rounded margin. Eyes large, with dark brown irides. Flight membranes black-brown.

Madagascar Sheath-tailed Bat *Coleura kibomalandy* DD
Emballonure à ventre blanc

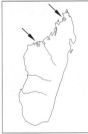

15–115 m

FA 48–52 mm, **W** 8·4–12·5 g.
Dry deciduous forests on lowland limestone karst.
Fur above long and shaggy, blackish-brown; below greyish-cream to pure white, often with grey on underfur. Wing membranes light to medium brown, often with relatively large translucent patches. Lacks radio-metacarpal and gular throat pouches.

MADAGASCAR SUCKER-FOOTED BATS Myzopodidae

Schliemann's Sucker-footed Bat *Myzopoda schliemanni* LC
Myzopode de Schliemann

0–200 m

FA 45–49 mm, **W** 7·8–10·3 g.
Lowland dry deciduous forest, often heavily degraded, with remnant vegetation and stands of Bismarck palms (*Bismarckia nobilis*); forages in open
grassland, particularly zones with marshland and open water.
Sucker-like structures on wrists and
ankles. Fur above fairly long, uniform
pale brown; below mouse-grey.
Upper lips extend beyond limit
of mandible and are flexible. Ear
markedly long and pointed,
with odd-shaped mushroom-
like structure at base. Wings
and uropatagium dark brown. Tail
protrudes beyond hind margin of tail membrane.

Eastern Sucker-footed Bat *Myzopoda aurita* LC
Myzopode de Madagascar

0–1000 m

FA 46–49 mm, **W** 9–9·5 g.
Lowland and littoral forests, often near margins or in degraded forest, and
large stands of traveller's palms (*Ravenala madagascariensis*) associated with
anthropogenic forest degradation.
Sucker-like structures on wrists and
ankles. Fur above fairly long, uniform
golden dark brown; below light brown.
Upper lips extend beyond limit of
mandible and are flexible. Ear
markedly long and pointed,
with odd-shaped mushroom-
like structure at base. Wings and
uropatagium dark brown. Tail
protrudes beyond hind margin of tail membrane.

FREE-TAILED BATS   Molossidae

Peters's Goblin Bat   *Mormopterus jugularis*   LC
Molosse de Madagascar

0–1750 m

FA 30–39 mm, **W** 8·5–17 g.
Wide variety of bioclimatic zones, from humid to arid forests, open woodland and degraded habitats.
Flattened head, no facial ornamentation; tail protrudes beyond hind margin of uropatagium. Fur short, soft and uniform brown to reddish-brown above, becoming pale brown to dirty white below. Ears small, subtriangular and separated at bases; tragus small but not concealed by antitragus. Adult male has distinct throat gland, absent in female. Upper lips have several wrinkles, a few spoon-hairs, and many fine hairs. Wings and uropatagium dark brown. Hindclaws have fine hairs and many stout bristles. Male larger than female.

Malagasy Large-eared Free-tailed Bat   *Otomops madagascariensis*   LC
Tadaride de Madagascar

0–1350 m

FA 57–63 mm, **W** 17·5–29·5 g.
Limestone and other sedimentary rocky habitats in vicinity of dry deciduous forests or spiny bush; also urban habitats.
Fur soft and dense; dark brown with dark rusty brown tinge, or blackish-brown, darker on head and body, with pale brown or white band across shoulders, and thin band of pale brown separating dark dorsal pelage from dark wing membrane on each side; belly dark brown, throat paler. Face pink, with pig-like snout; upper lip expansible, with many fine wrinkles and no spoon-hairs. Ears rounded and fairly stiff, projecting forwards well beyond snout; inner margins joined together and to muzzle; tragus minute; antitragus absent but a semicircular flap extends forwards from base of ear and can be folded down to seal ear opening; no interaural crest. Gular sac well developed. Wings and uropatagium blackish-brown. Male substantially larger than female.

Grandidier's Lesser Free-tailed Bat   *Chaerephon leucogaster*   NE
Tadaride de Grandidier

0–900 m

FA 33–37 mm, **W** 6–10 g.
Dry, open woodland; also degraded habitats and urban areas.
Smallest *Chaerephon* in Madagascar. Fur short; head, back, throat and chest dark brown, belly whitish. Ears medium-sized, joined by band of skin; tragus very small, squarish or sometimes with small lobe at top of rear margin, and concealed by semicircular antitragus; male has interaural crest and associated crest of long erectile hairs. No gular or tail glands. Wing and tail membranes typically blackish, but pale and translucent in some individuals.

Malagasy Eastern Free-tailed Bat *Chaerephon atsinanana* LC
Tadaride d'Atsinanana

0–1100 m

FA 37–42 mm, **W** 9–17 g.
Urban zones, agriculture and ecotone between forest and open areas.
Fur short, blackish-brown above, brown on throat, dark brown below, rarely with small white mid-ventral patch; often, a distinct whitish or beige stripe of longer hairs at flanks. Upper lip wrinkled. Ears large and rounded, dark brown; antitragus very broad, with angular anterior edge, and terminating in rectangular-blunt tip.

Malagasy Western Free-tailed Bat *Chaerephon jobimena* LC
Tadaride dimorphe

50–870 m

FA 45–48 mm, **W** 12–16 g.
Dry deciduous or spiny forests, usually associated with limestone and other sedimentary rocky outcrops.
Back and throat medium chocolate-brown, abruptly becoming light brownish-grey on belly, appearing indistinctly grizzled grey; rufous morph occurs. Upper lip has 5–6 well-defined wrinkles on each side. Ears notably longer than in other Malagasy *Chaerephon*; joined by V-shaped band of skin, but lacking interaural pocket or crest; minute tragus covered by lobe-shaped, slightly asymmetrical antitragus. Wing and tail membranes brownish-black. No gular or tail glands.

Midas's Free-tailed Bat *Mops midas* LC
Tadaride midas

0–150 m

FA 59–67 mm, **W** 38–69 g.
Woodland and grassland habitats, often associated with major rivers.
Fur short, silky and sparse, almost absent across shoulders.
Above dark brown to pale brown or pale grey, with pale grey or white frosting and flecking; below greyish-brown or pinkish-brown to silvery grey, with pale ventral flank-stripe but no mid-ventral markings; orange morph occurs. Upper lip has 5–6 well-defined wrinkles on each side and many spoon-hairs. Ears blackish-brown and relatively long; joined across forehead by interaural band of skin with erectile crest of long brown hairs; tragus small, squarish or hatchet-shaped, and concealed by large, semicircular antitragus. Wings medium brown, uropatagium dark brown.

Malagasy Large White-bellied Free-tailed Bat *Mops leucostigma* `LC`
Tadaride à giron blanc

FA 40–47 mm,
W 12–28 g.
Various habitats, from urban and agricultural areas to dry deciduous, humid evergreen, montane and degraded forests.
Fur short, almost absent between shoulders; greyish-brown or brownish above, beige or white below, with no contrasting mid-ventral markings or flank-stripe. Upper lip has 7–8 well-defined wrinkles on each side and many spoon-hairs. Ears relatively short, joined across forehead by interaural band of skin with erectile crest of hairs. Wings medium to dark grey. Male significantly larger than female, with more developed crest, and nostrils more elongated and flared.

0–1300 m

Malagasy Large Free-tailed Bat *Tadarida fulminans* `LC`
Tadaride de Thomas

FA 56–61 mm,
W 23–49 g.
Dry and moist savanna woodland, typically with rocky outcrops.
Sexually dimorphic: male reddish-brown above, fulvous pink below, with yellowish mid-ventral and flank stripes; female dark chocolate-brown above, white below. Upper lip lacks well-defined wrinkles; rather few spoon-hairs. Ears dark brown, relatively small, with inner margins meeting at base of forehead to form V-shaped valley; tragus large, roughly rectangular, and not concealed by antitragus, which is low, triangular and only slightly larger than tragus; no interaural crest. Gular gland naked and conspicuous, especially in male. Wing membranes and uropatagium brown above, whitish below. Undersides of forearms and legs naked and white; thumb and plantar (sole) pads present.

0–2000 m

Aellen's Long-fingered Bat   *Miniopterus aelleni*   LC
Minitoptère d'Aellen

FA 35–38 mm, **W** 3·7–5·4 g.
Deciduous forest, including "tsingy" habitat
in lowland areas associated with karst
limestone landscapes.
Above medium to dark brown, head
sometimes slightly lighter; below buff, mottled
darker. Uropatagium with sparse hairs. Tragus moderately long, broad at
base, with lateral flange that becomes reduced distally; slightly deflected,
tapering medially; distal tip forms blunt point or sometimes slightly
rounded; shaft of tragus distinctly wider proximally than in *M. manavi* and
M. griveaudi.

0–700 m

Griveaud's Long-fingered Bat   *Miniopterus griveaudi*   DD
Mitopère de Griveaud

FA 35–38 mm, **W** 4·1–7·1 g.
Lowland gallery forest and remnant forest
fragments surrounded by agricultural areas.
Generally dark brown above, sometimes
blackish (dark morph) or reddish-brown (red
morph); head usually slightly paler than back; below fur typically has grey-
ish-buff tips, giving mottled appearance. Tragus relatively thin, with straight
shaft, and sometimes reduced flange on exterior margin; terminates in
slightly retracted and rounded head. Wings generally dark to medium
brown, grading into lighter brown in section surrounding tail; uropatagium
largely naked, attached to femur and directly to ankle joint.

0–400 m

Glen's Long-fingered Bat   *Miniopterus gleni*   LC
Miniopère de Glen

FA 47–50 mm, **W** 10·5–17·5 g.
Various habitats, including humid
forest, dry deciduous forest and spiny
bush.
Amongst largest *Miniopterus* in Madagascar,
along with *M. griffithsi*. Above uniform
dark chocolate-brown, below uniform
chocolate-brown, slightly lighter towards
wing membranes, which are of same colour, as is uropatagium. Compared
with *M. griffithsi*, tragus lacks prominent flange to external edge, distal
two-thirds with inward curve, and distal tip rounded and slightly deflected
downwards.

0–1250 m

Short-tragus Long-fingered Bat *Miniopterus brachytragos* LC
Minioptère à oreillons courts

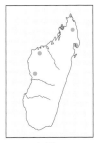

FA 35–38 mm, **W** 2·9–6·3 g.
Near native dry deciduous forest and disturbed humid lowland gallery forest.
Fur relatively short, not particularly dense.
Above medium to darkish brown; below,
hairs tipped dark buff, giving slightly mottled
appearance. Wing membranes medium brown, grading into slightly lighter
brown on uropatagium. Uropatagium attached to femur above ankle joint;
has relatively short, dense fur on most of dorsal surface, most obvious on
proximal half. Tragus short and thick, with rounded to slightly pointed tip;
distal part has a few long hairs (difficult to see with naked eye).

0–600 m

Malagasy Northern Long-fingered Bat *Miniopterus ambohitrensis* LC
Minioptère d'Ambohitra

FA 37–42 mm, **W** 5·3–7·7 g.
Upland mesic or montane humid forest.
Fur a mixture of medium and dark
brown; pectoral area and head often
with varying amounts of rufous brown
fur. Tragus moderately long , slightly
broader at base, with slight constriction
along mid-shaft; distal portion medially deflected; tip slightly rounded.
Differs from very similar *M. aelleni* in areas of rufous brown fur, slightly larger
size, and slightly shorter tragus.

800–1600 m

Major's Long-fingered Bat *Miniopterus majori* LC
Minioptère de Major

FA 43–47 mm, **W** 8·4–12·5 g.
Various habitats, including humid
forest and spiny bush.
Averages larger than very similar
M. sororculus; also darker above,
approaching rich, dark chocolate-
brown; below, slightly paler rich dark brown; tragus
slightly longer and with distinctly broader base, constricting towards mid-
section, then forming slightly arching structure to a rounded point.

0–1000 m

Eger's Long-fingered Bat *Miniopterus egeri* LC
Minioptère d'Eger

FA 37–40 mm, **W** 4·2–7·6 g.
Intact native forests to degraded
anthropogenic habitats.
Fur above and below fairly long and
dense; a mixture of medium to dark
brown interspersed with distinctly lighter brown. Wing membranes and
uropatagium uniform brownish-black and largely naked. Tragus thick along
shaft and slightly constricted on lower distal side; length of proximal edge
has distinct flange that folds slightly anterior-medially; downward-deflected
tip notably thickened and slightly fleshy. Differs from *M. petersoni* and
M. sororculus most notably in form of tragus.

0–1300 m

Manavi Long-fingered Bat *Miniopterus manavi* LC
Minioptère du Betsileo

FA 37·6–39·2 mm, **W** 6·4 g.
Continuous forest, irrigated lowland
rice paddies, secondary vegetation and
hillside rice.
Fur typically blackish, rather paler below
than above; rufous morph has fur dull red-
dish throughout; reddish-brown red morph has coal-black back and slightly
lighter belly. Wing membranes and uropatagium brownish-black, attached
to femur at same level above ankle joint; fur extends thinly over nearly
half of upper surface of uropatagium, sparser on proximal ventral surface.
Tragus relatively thin along distal two-thirds; medial margin has flange,
distal lateral portion slightly enlarged and rounded, and distal medial tip
terminates with angular straight edge.

900–1500 m

Small Sister Long-fingered Bat *Miniopterus sororculus* LC
Minioptère soeur

FA 42–45 mm, **W** 7–9·1 g.
Remnant native vegetation, open grassland and probably transformed and
degraded habitats.
Fur dense, relatively long and slightly
silky; rich dark brown above, occasionally approaching medium dark
brown; slightly paler below. Wing membranes
and uropatagium uniform brownish-black;
fur extends sparsely onto wing membranes,
especially nearest body. Tragus relatively long, with curved projection and
laterally thickened base.

40–2200 m
(mostly above 900 m)

Peterson's Long-fingered Bat *Miniopterus petersoni* DD
Mioptère de Peterson

0–550 m

FA 38–43 mm, **W** 4·2–8·2 g.
Humid lowland forest, littoral forest and transitional dry and humid formations; also gallery forest and around ecotone between forest and secondary habitats.
Fur rather long and dense; above and below, a mixture of medium brown and dark brown. Wing membranes and uropatagium uniform brownish-black. Tragus has relatively long-curved projection, and notable constriction on lower distal surface; distal one-third has pronounced downward deflection, and lower surface has distinct notch, whereas *M. sororculus* lacks notch and tends to be less deflected.

Mahafaly Long-fingered Bat *Miniopterus mahafaliensis* LC
Mioptère du Mahafaly

0–950 m

FA 35–40 mm, **W** 3·8–7·3 g.
Within or adjacent to dry deciduous forests or spiny bush; not thought to be forest-dependent.
Fur relatively long and dense; above medium brown; below appears notably paler due to light-grey-tipped hairs. Wing membranes medium brown, grading into slightly lighter brown on uropatagium; latter has relatively dense fur on dorsal surface and sparser fur on ventral surface. Tragus moderately wide and has parallel margins along most of its length; distal part curves medially into slightly expanded and rounded tip.

Griffiths's Long-fingered Bat *Miniopterus griffithsi* DD
Mioptère de Griffiths

0–110 m

FA 48–50 mm, **W** 12–15·5 g.
Probably open habitats or close to forest edge.
Amongst largest *Miniopterus* in Madagascar, along with *M. gleni*. Upper back distinctly lighter brown than middle and lower back, which approach medium brown; below, a mixture of mainly lighter brown (particularly towards wing membrane), with interspersed medium brown. Wing membranes and uropatagium dark brown, with notable light spotting on uropatagium. Tragus relatively long and thickset, with distinct flange on distal half of external surface and slightly tapered downward deflection on inner edge; distal end not particularly rounded, giving slightly squarish terminal edge.

Rüppell's Bat *Vansonia rueppellii* [LC]
Pipistrelle de Rüppell

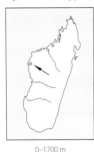

0–1700 m

FA 28–37 mm, **W** 4–9 g.
Disturbed partially flooded marshland dominated by *Bismarckia* palms. Only recently recorded in Madagascar.

Fur soft, dense and slick; above grey to pale greyish-brown or sepia brown, occasionally with silvery sheen; below pure white, with throat pure white or pale rusty brown. Face and ears blackish. Ears relatively long; tragus half ear length, with slightly concave anterior margin, constant breadth, and rounded tip. Wings whitish to medium brown, typically translucent pale grey. Uropatagium pale grey; extends to end of tail; calcar reaches about halfway across uropatagium.

Dusky Pipistrelle *Pipistrellus hesperidus* [LC]
Pipistrelle hespéride

5–35 m

FA 27–38 mm, **W** 3·5–9 g.
Lowlands, often in or near dry deciduous forest, but also in more degraded areas; typically near water.
Fur dense and soft, coloration very variable; above pale greyish-brown or reddish-brown to darker brown or nearly black; below cream or creamy orange to orange-red, reddish-brown or dark brown. Naked face dark brown. Ears dark reddish-brown, with rounded tips. Tragus widest just below mid-height, with rounded tip, and nearly straight anteriorly; posterior margin smoothly convex, with small basal lobe. Wing membrane pale brown to blackish-brown, being darker or lighter in line with fur colour; no white hind border. Uropatagium paler than wing membrane, stretching roughly to tail tip from calcar.

Racey's Pipistrelle *Pipistrellus raceyi* [DD]
Pipistrelle de Racey

10–300 m

FA 27–33 mm, **W** 3·8–5·8 g.
Relatively intact and degraded deciduous forest in west; near disturbed lowland and humid forest or agriculture in east.
Generally larger in east than in west.
Fur above light rufous, with distinctly darker head; below buffy brown. Wing membranes and uropatagium brownish-black; latter stretches roughly to end of tail. Muzzle relatively short and inflated, with large, essentially naked glandular swellings; face pinkish, but blackish-brown closer to front of muzzle. Ears uniform brownish-black and short, with rounded tips and 3–5 well-developed ridges; tragus c. 50% height of ear, crescent-shaped, with small notch near base of posterior border, and rounded tip.

Dark Madagascar Pipistrelle *Neoromicia bemainty* `LC`
Vespère de Kirindy

0–870 m

FA 29–32 mm, **W** 2·8–4·4 g.
Various forested and non-forested habitats, including dry forest and human-altered areas.
Fur shaggy; above dark chocolate-brown to dark tan with some grey streaking; below medium tan (hairs with dark bases). Bare parts of face, wings, uropatagium and ears dark brown (ventral surface of wings sometimes has white venation). Ear subtriangular with rounded tip, with moderately long hair on proximal half of dorsal surface; tragus parallel for proximal half and then tapers medially towards rounded tip. Tail more or less surrounded to tip by uropatagium.

Malagasy Serotine *Laephotis matroka* `LC`
Vespère de Madagascar

970–1300 m

FA 29–35 mm, **W** c. 9 g.
Around humid forests, open agricultural areas and anthropogenic grassland.
Fur dense and soft; above dark brown; below brownish-grey, paler on belly. Ears triangular with rounded tips; tragus less than half ear length and wider at mid-height, with convex posterior margin and rounded tip. Wings very dark.

Isalo Serotine *Laephotis malagasyensis* `VU`
Vespère de l'Isalo

450–700 m

FA 30·1–32 mm.
Found foraging over water in transitional tropical dry gallery forest in canyons.
Fur above dark brown; below sharply bicoloured, with a mixture of dark buff and grey, becoming paler towards tail. Ears mid-brown and translucent.

Roberts's Serotine   *Laephotis robertsi*   DD
Vespère de Roberts

900–1300 m

FA 34·5–38 mm.
Known only from partially degraded habitats at two localities: Anjozorobe-Angavo and Mantadia-Analamazaotra (Andasibe-Mantadia National Park). Fur above and below dark chocolate-brown; below, outer fur of upper chest often has slightly lighter sheen, giving impression of being bicoloured. Ears blackish-brown; lower proximal half of ear furred; tragus less than 50% of ear length, outer margins parallel for about two-thirds of proximal length before curving slightly, finishing in rounded tip. Wings and uropatagium blackish-brown.

Malagasy Western House Bat   *Scotophilus tandrefana*   DD
Scotophile d'Andadoany

0–100 m

FA 44–47 mm, **W** c. 14 g.
Poorly known; apparently linked to dry deciduous forest. Fur above long and soft, dark chocolate-brown, with basal parts distinctly lighter brown; fur below shorter and finer, lighter medium brown, with greyish-brown bases. Wings and uropatagium brownish-black. Ears short and black; tragus long, projecting forward, with complex peduncle, and slightly rounded tip. Muzzle relatively short, but pronounced and rounded; nostrils slightly elongated, opening antero-laterally.

Marovaza House Bat   *Scotophilus marovaza*   LC
Scotophile de Marovaza

0–200 m

FA 41–45 mm, **W** 12·5–16·8 g.
Ecotones of grassland and disturbed lowland dry deciduous forest, in and around villages, open areas close to natural forest, and dry riverbeds at margins of slightly disturbed dry deciduous forest. Fur relatively short; above reddish-brown, with distinctly paler brownish-red band across central back; below uniform shiny light brownish-yellow. Wings and uropatagium brownish-black. Muzzle short, broad and pug-like; distinct rostral swelling in front of eyes; nostril openings crescent-shaped and outward-pointing. Tragus long and sickle-shaped, tapering to fine point at apex, outer margin convex, with circular lobe at base; antitragus well developed, slightly asymmetrical and semi-round, separated from ear by distinct notch.

Malagasy Large House Bat *Scotophilus robustus* LC
Scotophile robuste

FA 62–65 mm,
W c. 40·5–49 g.
All habitats, except spiny bush.
Fur above and below medium brown. Large-headed but short-snouted; sagittal crest well developed; forehead slightly concave.

0–1400 m

Malagasy Mouse-eared Bat *Myotis goudotii* LC
Murin de Madagascar

FA 37–40 mm, **W** 5–6 g.
Wide range of different vegetation types, but appears to favour forest; undergrowth and partially open areas used for foraging.
Fur soft and thick; above dark brown (hairs with light brownish bases and dark tips); below dark greyish or ash-brown (hairs with dark brown bases and brownish-grey or ash tips). Head somewhat flattened, with short, triangular muzzle, occasionally with pronounced proximal indentation; face densely covered in long hairs. Ears medium-sized; tragus narrow, long and pointed, reaching about half ear length. Calcar relatively long; lacks lobe.

0–1200 m

RIGHT AND BOWHEAD WHALES Balaenidae

Southern Right Whale *Eubalaena australis* LC
Baleine australe

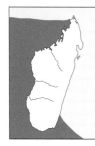

TL 1500–1650 cm, **W** up to c. 60,000 kg.
Pelagic; gives birth in coastal areas, in sheltered shallow waters and bays. Massive and stocky, head extremely large. Generally black, but with pale greyish area on back and white patches on lower jaws and belly. No dorsal fin or ridge. Flukes wide, tapering gently to smooth trailing edges. Prevalent callosities on head and rostral region. Can appear mottled whitish or pale grey due to sloughing of skin.

RORQUALS Balaenopteridae

Humpback Whale *Megaptera novaeangliae* LC
Rorqual à bosse

TL 1500–1700 cm, **W** 30,000–34,000 kg.
Pelagic, but mother-offspring pairs show strong preference for near off-shore reef systems, islands, channels and continental-shelf areas. Shorter and stouter than other rorquals; pectoral flipper very large. Distinctly countershaded, dorsal side uniformly black, ventral surface ranging from black to white or mottled black and white. Dorsal fin relatively small. Blow fairly low and bushy, generally up to 2–3 m high.

Fin Whale *Balaenoptera physalus* VU
Rorqual commun

TL 2200–2700 cm, **W** 60,000–90,000 kg.
Pelagic and continental-shelf waters.
Distinctive asymmetrical head coloration: left side of head, including lower lip, uniformly dark grey like body; right lower lip and right inside of mouth white. Often a greyish-white chevron on upper back behind blowholes, with apex of chevron pointing forwards. Dorsal fin distinct, up to 60 cm long. Breaches more often than other large rorquals. Surface blow cone-shaped, reaching up to 6 m.

Blue Whale *Balaenoptera musculus* EN
Rorqual bleu

TL 3170–3260 cm, **W** 113,000–150,000 kg.
Generally pelagic, but sometimes in neritic areas.
The largest animal. Head uniform grey, body generally light bluish-grey with extensive grey to greyish-white mottling; ventral surface lighter. Dorsal fin tiny, distinctly triangular to broadly rounded or smoothly falcate. When surfacing, it first shows head and blowholes, then broad back, and finally diminutive dorsal fin. Blow typically tall, slender and distinctly vertical (9–12 m high).

Sei Whale *Balaenoptera borealis* EN
Rorqual boréal

TL 1700–2000 cm, **W** 22,000–38,000 kg.
Temperate pelagic waters.
Dark steel-grey on back, with bluish shade; below slightly lighter with irregular, greyish-white patch near ventral groove blubber. Pectoral flipper and caudal flukes relatively small. Dorsal fin relatively tall and strongly falcate. When diving, rarely raises tail flukes above water or arches its back. Blow tall and columnar to bushy, generally up to 3–4 m high.

111

Bryde's Whale *Balaenoptera edeni* `LC`
Rorqual d'Eden

TL 1050–1450 cm, **W** 15,000–16,600 kg.
Warm temperate neritic and pelagic waters.
Three rostral ridges, with prominent median ridge, as in other rorquals, and shorter lateral ridges. Bluish-black dorsally, white or yellowish ventrally, with bluish-grey area extending onto ventral groove blubber and flippers. Dorsal fin relatively large and strongly falcate, with distinctly tapering tip. Breaches more often than most other rorquals. Blow columnar to bushy, up to 3–4 m high.

southern

northern

Omura's Whale *Balaenoptera omurai* `DD`
Rorqual d'Omura

TL 1000–1200 cm.
Pelagic and inshore waters.
Distinctly counter-shaded, blue-black to dark grey above, whitish-beige to cream-coloured below. Undersides of pectoral flippers and caudal flukes also pale. Coloration of lower jaws asymmetrical: black to dark grey on left, whitish-beige to cream-coloured on right. Single prominent median ridge, extending from blowholes to tip of rostrum.

Common Minke Whale *Balaenoptera acutorostrata* `LC`
Petit Rorqual

TL 650–880 cm, **W** 2000–2700 kg.
Mainly pelagic, but more frequent than other rorquals in inshore waters and even up large rivers.
Dark bluish-grey back, ivory-white below, with streaks or lobes of lighter transitional shading. Roughly symmetrical pair of prominent pale grey arched streaks extend from just above flippers to back; distinctive brilliant white patch across middle of dorsal surface of pectoral flipper. Dorsal fin relatively large, typically falcate. Blow low (1–2 m high), bushy and rather inconspicuous.

Antarctic Minke Whale *Balaenoptera bonaerensis* NT
Rorqual antarctique

TL 840–1020 cm, **W** 6800–11,000 kg.
Mainly pelagic and beyond continental shelf break.
Similar to *B. acutorostrata*, but larger. Two light grey wavy streaks extend backwards down sides from near blowhole. Slim, pointed pectoral flippers typically solid grey. Dorsal fin relatively tall, typically falcate. When swimming at sea, blowhole and large dorsal fin typically visible together when an individual surfaces. Blow low, generally 1–2 m high, and bushy.

SPERM WHALE Physeteridae

Sperm Whale *Physeter macrocephalus* VU
Grand Cachalot

TL 1040–1920 cm, **W** up to more than 70,000 kg (male much larger than female).
Deep ice-free ocean waters.
Dark grey, but can appear dark brown in bright sunlight. Enormous head constitutes c. 25–33% of total length. Single blowhole located asymmetrically on left side at front end of rostrum. Conical teeth erupt only on narrow, under-slung lower jaw. Flat, paddle-shaped flippers and large, triangular flukes with relatively straight trailing edges. Blow small, directed towards left.

♀

♂

Pygmy Sperm Whale   *Kogia breviceps* LC
Cachalot pygmée

TL 270–420 cm, **W** 342–680 kg.
Deep water, typically seaward of continental shelf.
Generally blackish-brown above, shading to cream on belly. Height of dorsal fin less than 5% of body length. Distance between snout and anterior insertion of dorsal fin greater than 50% of total body length. Lower jaw has 12–16 (rarely 10–11) teeth on each side; generally none in upper jaw.

Dwarf Sperm Whale   *Kogia sima* LC
Cachalot nain

TL 200–270 cm, **W** 136–280 kg.
Continental shelf and slope, frequently in waters with depths of 900–1500 m.
Generally blackish-brown dorsally, shading to cream on belly. Dorsal fin greater than 5% of total length, and taller than that of *K. breviceps*. Shorter snout than *K. breviceps*; distance between snout and anterior insertion of dorsal fin less than 50% of total length. Lower jaw has 8–13 teeth on each side; up to three in each side of upper jaw.

BEAKED WHALES Ziphiidae

Cuvier's Beaked Whale *Ziphius cavirostris* LC
Baleine-à-bec de Cuvier

TL 600–700 cm, **W** 2500–3500 kg.
Deep oceanic waters, and generally in areas with water depth greater than 500 m.
Short beak. Flukes wide, tailstock compressed laterally. Dorsal fin small and set approximately two-thirds of distance between tip of beak and end of tail. Coloration typically dark brown or dark grey. Adults of both sexes may have paler head; in adult male, pale head usually very distinct. Dorsal surface of adult male may be covered in pale linear scars.

♀

grey morph

♂

brown morph

Longman's Beaked Whale *Indopacetus pacificus* LC
Baleine-à-bec de Longman

TL 565–650 cm, **W** c. 7500 kg.
Deeper oceanic waters.
Dark brown to dark grey or black. Body spindle-shaped, with greatest girth around midpoint; flukes wide in relation to body length; tailstock laterally compressed. Dorsal fin set approximately two-thirds of distance between tip of beak and end of tail. Rostrum and lower jaw form short but well-defined beak; two grooves on throat. Teeth comprise single pair of tusks at tip of lower jaw (only in male).

True's Beaked Whale *Mesoplodon mirus* LC
Baleine-à-bec de True

TL 480–540 cm, **W** 1000–1400 kg.
Mainly waters more than 200 m deep.
Body spindle-shaped, with greatest girth around midpoint. Medium to dark grey above, paler below, with dark patch behind eye; white or pale area on each flank from dorsal fin backwards; adult male can have long white, unpigmented scars from aggressive male–male interactions. Flukes wide in relation to body length, tailstock laterally compressed. Dorsal fin small and set about two-thirds of the way back from tip of beak to tip of tail. Rostrum and lower jaw form short but distinct beak; two grooves on throat; adult male has pair of conical tusks at tip of rostrum.

Gray's Beaked Whale *Mesoplodon grayi* LC
Baleine-à-bec de Gray

TL 450–500 cm, **W** c. 900 kg.
Deep oceanic waters. Not yet recorded for Madagascar, but present nearby. Long, distinct beak; two grooves on throat. Coloration typically dark brown, dark grey or black; paler on ventral surface. Adult male has linear scars. Flukes wide, tailstock compressed laterally. Dorsal fin small and set approximately two-thirds of distance between tip of beak and end of tail. Adult males have single tusk on each side of lower jaw.

Blainville's Beaked Whale *Mesoplodon densirostris* `LC`
Baleine-à-bec de Blainville

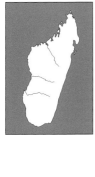

TL 425–475 cm, **W** c. 800 kg.
Deep oceanic waters.
Distinct beak; two grooves on throat. Overall dark brown to dark grey
or black; female and juvenile may be paler on ventral surface, adult
male darker. Adult male has linear scars. Flukes wide, tailstock laterally
compressed. Dorsal fin small and set approximately two-thirds of distance
between tip of beak and end of tail. Lower jaw distinctively arched; in adult
male, arching enhanced to raise tusks above height of upper jaw and head.

♀

♂

Killer Whale *Orcinus orca* `DD`
Épaulard

TL up to 980 cm, **W** up to 6600 kg (male larger than female).
All marine habitats; more abundant in inshore waters; rarely river mouths.
Distinctive. Body robust but streamlined, with tall dorsal fin (especially male), large paddle-shaped flippers, and blunt, poorly defined beak. Mainly black; white patch above eye; lower jaw and ventral area to urogenital region white, with lobe curving up onto each flank between genital slit and dorsal fin; underside of flukes white; grey saddle patch behind dorsal fin. Sometimes a distinctive grey line extends from lower point of saddle patch towards head, creating a curved "cape" shape. White areas can appear yellowish due to build-up of diatoms.

Rough-toothed Dolphin *Steno bredanensis* `LC`
Dauphin sténo

TL up to 280 cm, **W** up to 155 kg.
Prefers deep offshore waters beyond continental shelf but also found in shallow coastal waters.
Robust, with conical head, distinguished by lack of clear demarcation between beak and melon. Most of body dark grey, with narrow darker dorsal cape that dips onto flanks below dorsal fin; belly, throat and lower jaw pinkish-white, separation not clearly defined; lips whiter. Large, slender flippers, with rounded tips; medium-sized falcate dorsal fin.

Risso's Dolphin *Grampus griseus* `LC`
Grampus

TL 380–410 cm, **W** 400–500 kg.
Warm, deep oceanic waters.
Robust body, with narrow tailstock; bulbous, squarish head, with barely discernible beak. Heavily scarred, with white scratches and blotches covering most of body; underlying skin dark to pale grey, with white patches on venter. Young usually darker. Unique deep vertical cleft or groove runs along anterior side of rostrum and melon. Flippers sickle-shaped; dorsal fin tall and falcate.

variants

False Killer Whale *Pseudorca crassidens* `NT`
Fausse-orque

TL 510–610 cm, **W** up to 2200 kg (male larger than female).
Primarily deep offshore waters.
Slender shape with rounded but not markedly bulbous head; no beak. Overall dark grey to black, with pale grey patch on chest. Flippers have rounded tips and distinct bulge on leading edge, which gives them a slight "S" shape. Dorsal fin small and falcate; tailstock deep.

Pygmy Killer Whale *Feresa attenuata* LC
Orque pygmée

TL 210–260 cm, **W** up to 225 kg.

Offshore deep water, associated with warm currents.

Dark grey to black, with narrow dark dorsal cape that dips below dorsal fin, contrasting with slightly paler grey flanks. Lips pale grey to white; narrow white patch runs ventrally along body, widening at urogenital area. Head bulbous and rounded, with no visible beak; flippers slender and slightly curved, with rounded tips. Dorsal fin tall and falcate. Many adults have scars over back and flanks, caused by sharks.

Melon-headed Whale *Peponocephala electra* LC
Péponocéphale

TL up to 280 cm, **W** up to 275 kg.

Deep offshore waters; also coastal regions, but only where continental shelf lies close to shore.

Differs from very similar *Feresa attenuata* by more triangular head and more sharply pointed flippers. Overall dark grey, with darker cape along back dipping below dorsal fin. Sometimes a dark band from blowhole forwards along melon, and dark eye patches from eyes towards front of melon, resulting in mask-like appearance.

Long-finned Pilot Whale *Globicephala melas* LC
Globicéphale noir

TL 570– 670 cm, **W** 1300–2300 kg (male larger than female).

Coastal and oceanic waters, apparently preferring habitat over continental shelf breaks and slopes. Not yet recorded for Madagascar, but present nearby.

Bulbous head; slight, barely visible beak; deep tailstock. Separated from *G. macrorhynchus* by very long flippers (18–27% of total body length), which curve to form pronounced "elbow." Skin pigmentation ranges from dark grey or brown to black, with several white or pale grey patches, notably chest patch, saddle behind dorsal fin, and eyebrow streaks; eyebrows and saddle sometimes connected by thin grey lines. Dorsal fin falcate, with wide base.

Short-finned Pilot Whale *Globicephala macrorhynchus* `LC`
Globicéphale tropical

TL 550–720 cm, **W** 1500–3500 kg (male larger than female).
Coastal and offshore waters, preferring deeper (600–1000 m) offshore
habitat.
Bulbous head, small beak and deep tailstock; falcate dorsal fin with wide
base. Overall black to dark grey or brown, with white or pale grey patches
on chest and urogenital area, behind dorsal fin, and above eyes; thin white
mid-ventral line may join chest and urogenital patches. Differs from rather
similar *G. melas* most notably in shorter flippers (14–19% of total body
length).

Indian Ocean Humpback Dolphin *Sousa plumbea* `EN`
Dauphin de Chine

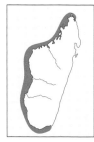

TL up to 280 cm, **W** up to 250–280 kg.
Typically coastal waters less than 20 m deep; usually found in estuarine
and inshore waters with rocky substrates, also mangrove swamps, coastal
lagoons, rocky or coral reefs and deep-water channels.
Medium-sized, robust body; long, narrow beak, with indistinct junction to
medium-sized melon. Dorsal fin small and sharply recurved, with broad
hump. Above dark grey, below whitish, usually with little or no spotting
above or below; young generally pale all over; some adults lose their dark
pigmentation, sometimes becoming all-white or pinkish. Male averages
slightly larger than female.

Common Bottlenose Dolphin *Tursiops truncatus* `LC`
Grand Dauphin

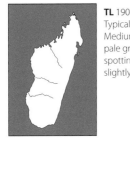

TL 190–380 cm, **W** 136–635 kg.
Typically along coasts and over continental shelf.
Medium-sized and robust, with short, robust beak and distinct crease. Body pale grey to black dorsally and laterally, with pale, sometimes pinkish belly; spotting rare. Dorsal fin tall and moderately falcate; flippers recurved and slightly pointed at tip. Deep-water form darker and more robust.

coastal

offshore

Indo-Pacific Bottlenose Dolphin *Tursiops aduncus* `NT`
Dauphin indien

TL 270 cm, **W** 230 kg.
Inshore waters and areas with sandy or rocky bottoms, coral reefs or seagrass beds.
Similar to *T. truncatus*, but appears more slender, with longer, thinner beak, slightly less convex melon, and more pointed head profile; dorsal fin, flippers and flukes generally broader and larger relative to body size. Dorsally dark grey, extending onto tailstock, and transitioning laterally until pale grey to off-white on ventral side; sometimes a pale spinal blaze, extending to below dorsal fin; belly with black spotting
(rare in *T. truncatus*).

Pantropical Spotted Dolphin *Stenella attenuata* LC
Dauphin bridé

TL 160–260 cm, **W** up to 119 kg.
Offshore, often around oceanic islands.
Slender body, with long, thin beak. Countershaded pattern underlies variable white spotting. Skin pale grey except for dark grey dorsal cape that sweeps low over flanks. Dorsal fin medium-sized, narrow and falcate, with pointed tip. Flippers slender and curved, also with pointed tips. In youngest stage, pale grey areas of adult replaced with white; no spotting.

Striped Dolphin *Stenella coeruleoalba* LC
Dauphin bleu et blanc

TL 216–256 cm, **W** 131–156 kg.
Prefers deep water; sometimes near coast, but only in deep water.
Robust *Stenella*. Fairly long beak separated from melon by crease. Three-toned pattern, with dark bluish-grey dorsal cape, pale grey flanks, and whitish-pink ventral surface; pale grey streak along flanks. Beak mostly black; thin stripe from beak to black ring around eye, broadening to flipper joint. Medium-sized, falcate dorsal fin; slender, curved dark grey flippers, with tapered and pointed tips.

Spinner Dolphin *Stenella longirostris* LC
Dauphin à long bec

TL 129–280 cm, **W** up to 80 kg.
Inshore waters of islands; also reefs and banks.
Slender, with very long, thin beak and slender, curved flippers; medium-sized dorsal fin falcate to triangular; sometimes a variable post-anal keel (especially in older males). Beak tip and lips dark grey; body three-toned, with dark grey dorsal cape, paler grey flanks, and white (pink-tinged) belly, throat and lower jaw; usually a dark stripe from eye to flipper joint.

Common Dolphin *Delphinus delphis* LC
Dauphin du Cap

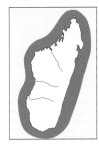

TL 193–260 cm, **W** up to 235 kg.
Coastal, usually within 180 km of shore, preferring shallow warm water less than 180 m deep.
Long beak. Dorsal surface dark grey to brown; belly white. Flanks have hourglass pattern, with pale grey (or yellowish) forward patch and less conspicuous, darker grey patch on tailstock; distinct dark stripe from flipper to anus. Lips black, dark stripe extends from chin to flipper joint, another dark stripe runs along crease between beak and melon and encircles eyes. Dorsal fin moderately tall and falcate, with pointed tip; flippers small and slender, also with pointed tips.

Fraser's Dolphin *Lagenodelphis hosei* LC
Dauphin de Fraser

TL up to 270 cm, **W** over 210 kg.
Mainly offshore waters over 1000 m deep, but also near shore.
Robust, stocky build; short, nearly triangular, slightly falcate dorsal fin (more triangular in male); and small, slender flippers with pointed tips. Beak short and stubby but well defined. Back and flanks dark grey or brown; belly, throat and lower jaw white, sometimes with pinkish tinge. Dark facemask and characteristic dark lateral stripe.

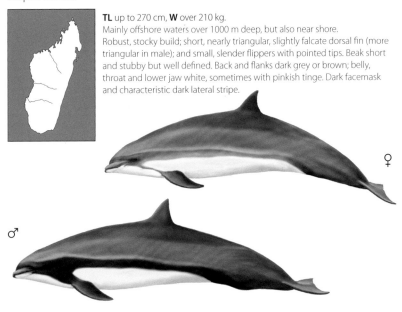

MADAGASCAR CARNIVORES Eupleridae

Fosa *Cryptoprocta ferox* VU
Fossa de Madagascar

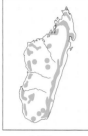

0–2600 m

HB 70–80 cm, **T** 65–70 cm, **W** 5·5–8·6 kg.
Mainly forest, including lowland dry deciduous forest in west and lowland rainforest in east; less common at higher altitudes.
Sleek, muscular body, long torso, and tail nearly equivalent to head-body length; male larger than female. Muzzle relatively short; ears short and rounded. Fur fine and relatively dense; above uniform pale reddish-brown; below dirty cream; belly sometimes stained orange by gland secretions, especially
in male.

Spotted Fanaloka *Fossa fossana* VU
Fossane

0–1300 m

HB 40–45 cm, **T** 22·1–26·4 cm, **W** 1·3–1·9 kg.
Various habitats; commonest in humid eastern forests, usually near water-courses; also dry deciduous forest in limestone canyons, and littoral forests. Civet-like, with short legs, pointed snout, bushy tail and large body. Fur dense, above tan to light brown with two nearly continuous black mid-dorsal lines, bordered by row of partially-broken stripes; below them is a row of spots on flanks; also scattered spots on flanks; throat, lower neck and rest of underparts cream to pale orange. Tail medium brown with concentric rings and spots.

Falanouc *Eupleres goudotii* VU
Euplère de Goudot

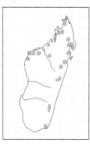

50–1600 m

HB 45·5–65 cm, **T** 22–25 cm, **W** 1·6–4·6 kg.
Seems to prefer upland humid forest with aquatic habitats, and areas of marsh; few observations in dense mesic forests away from wetlands. Massive elongated body, with long, narrow rostrum, prominent ears, large feet and short, rounded, tapered tail. Non-retractable claws on forelimbs well developed; when walking, claws touch ground, giving slow and saun-tering gait. Fur dense and soft, uniform reddish-brown above, brownish-beige below. Western populations darker, dark brown grizzled grey; thighs and underparts often with orange
tinge.

125

Ring-tailed Vontsira *Galidia elegans* `LC`
Galidie à queue annelée

0–1950 m

HB 30–38 cm, **T** 26–29·1 cm, **W** 655–965 g.

Most kinds of natural forest; sometimes short distances from relatively intact forest, in secondary forest and even in clearings. In far north, humid forest on lateritic soil, as well as areas of mixed mesic-dry deciduous forest in exposed karst. In west, canyons in limestone areas, and zones with relatively mesic habitat.

Mongoose-like, with relatively short feet and fluffy, furred tail slightly more than two-thirds of head–body length. Coloration varies geographically but also individually, with darkest forms in east, generally paler in north and west; body reddish-chestnut to dark chestnut, throat fulvous, top and sides of head fulvous grizzled black; underbody, flanks and feet reddish-chestnut to nearly black. Tail with alternating dark reddish-brown and almost black bands (5–7 of each). Ears clearly visible, but not prominent; edged paler.

Feet relatively large, with well-developed naked footpads; webbing at bases of toes; hindfeet longer than forefeet; claws not retractable; due to these adaptations, species able to run on ground, climb trees and swim.

north

east

Broad-striped Vontsira *Galidictis fasciata* `VU`
Galidie à bandes larges

0–1500 m

HB 30–48 cm, **T** 24·9–32·6 cm, **W** 520–1500 g.

Humid lowland to montane forest; most records from relatively intact forest, but also reported in degraded forest; not known from littoral forest on sandy substrates.

Mongoose-like, with relatively short feet and unicoloured furred tail, slightly over two-thirds of head–body length. Fur greyish-beige above, extending to feet and proximal portion of tail, and marked with distinct dark brown longitudinal bands. Head grizzled greyish-brown; below distinctly paler. Individuals from south-west (race *grandidieri*) much larger; dark brown longitudinal bands noticeably narrower.

most of range

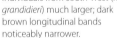

south-west (*grandidieri*)

Brown-tailed Vontsira *Salanoia concolor* VU
Galidie unicolore

200–750 m

HB 35–38 cm, **T** 16–20 cm, **W** 780 g.
Lowland tropical humid forest, both intact and degraded; also known from one marsh. Sleeps in burrows or hollow trees.
Uniformly darker than rather similar *Galidia elegans*, the two being sympatric. Fur above short and dark, with pale-tipped hairs giving agouti appearance; underside, including inner thighs, reddish-brown merging to whitish-grey around chin and mouth. Tail shorter than head–body length, and slightly bushy; uniform dark brown.

Bokyboky *Mungotictis decemlineata* EN
Galidie à dix raies

0–400 m

HB 26·4–33·5 cm, **T** 19·1–21·5 cm, **W** 450–740 g.
Dry deciduous forest on sandy substrates, often dominated by baobabs (*Adansonia*); prefers larger tracts of intact forest, commonly with dense understorey.
Distinctive, with long, pointed snout, cylindrical body, short legs and long bushy tail. Fur above grizzled grey mixed with light brown or beige, with 8–10 broadly spaced, thin longitudinal stripes running from nape to base of tail; underside and legs uniform pale brownish-beige to pale orangish-brown; pale grey tail lacks stripes or rings. Ears short and rounded. Webbing between toes; claws long. Populations of south-west darker above, with darker, more distinct stripes, which start higher on nape; underside distinctly darker, almost russet.

Mammals of the Comoros, the Seychelles, Réunion and Mauritius

Land mammals occurring naturally in neighbouring island groups.

	Comoros[a]	Seychelles	Réunion	Mauritius[b]
Endemic				
Rousettus obliviosus	x			
Pteropus livingstonii	x			
Pteropus rodricensis				x
Pteropus aldabrensis		x		
Pteropus seychellensis	x	x		
Pteropus niger			x	x
Paratriaenops pauliani		x		
Coleura seychellensis		x		
Mormopterus francoismoutoui			x	
Mormopterus acetabulosus				x
Chaerephon pusillus		x		
Scotophilus borbonicus			x	
Myotis anjouanensis	x			
Non-endemic				
Taphozous mauritianus[1]	x	x	x	x
Chaerephon leucogaster[2]	x			
Mops leucostigma[3]	x			
Miniopterus aelleni[4]	x			
Miniopterus griveaudi[4]	x			

[a] = including Mayotte, [b] = with Rodrigues
[1] see page 96; [2] see page 99; [3] see page 101; [4] see page 102.

OLD WORLD FRUIT BATS   Pteropodidae

Comoro Rousette   *Rousettus obliviosus*   VU
Roussette des Comores

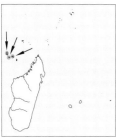

FA 70–78 mm, **W** 42–73 g.
Widely distributed in now limited tropical moist forest and agricultural land; very tolerant of man-modified landscapes. Roosts in caves.
Similar in size to *R. madagascariensis* (see page 93), but with more robust skull and strongly deflected braincase. Fur dull grey-brown. Dorsal side of tibia naked.

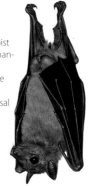

0–1750 m

Livingstone's Flying Fox   *Pteropus livingstonii*   CR
Roussette de Livingstone

40–1200 m

FA 161–172 mm, **W** c. 575–600 g.
Mainly undisturbed moist forest; less frequent in degraded forest. Roosts in emergent trees on steep-sided, south-east-facing slopes (perhaps sensitive to wind and sun).
Largest *Pteropus* in western Indian Ocean. Head fox-like, with muzzle long and black. Eyes relatively large, with orange to scarlet irides. Ears large, semicircular above and protruding; inner margin convex, outer margin straight or slightly convex; exposed concha smooth, without ribs or grooves. Fur blackish-brown on head and body, with dark russet tinge on back and belly; above and below speckled with golden or tawny hairs; tawny-tipped hairs form band across mantle, with similar tufts on shoulders; genital area sometimes encircled by ring of deep reddish-brown, extending laterally as a short stripe. Dense fur on upper inside of femur and uropatagium; upper side of tibia naked. Wings dark, often jet-black, shiny and hairless; index claw present; tail membrane poorly developed.

Rodrigues Flying Fox   *Pteropus rodricensis*   EN
Roussette de Rodrigues

0–400 m

FA 121–128·5 mm, **W** 278 g (mean).
Primary and secondary forest; occasionally rural areas dominated by introduced plants.
Muzzle short and narrow; rhinarium black, with short tubular nostrils and median furrow. Eyes small and close together, with brown irides. Ears very short, almost concealed in fur, wide at base, and pointed. Fur long and silky; head brown, sometimes with paler patch on forehead; mantle rich ochraceous orange, fading to cream buff posteriorly; back dark brown to blackish, sometimes conspicuously frosted; chest ochraceous brown, belly brown and frosted, anal region paler; genitals black, concealed in fur. Tibia dark and furred. Wing membranes black, originating from sides of body, slightly above medial plane. Uropatagium reduced; calcar small.

Aldabra Flying Fox *Pteropus aldabrensis* EN
Roussette d'Aldabra

0–20 m

FA 128–141 mm, **W** 257–395 g.
Dry scrub and dry woodland. Roosts in *Casuarina*, mangroves and plantations.
Snout greyish-brown; head bright yellowish-ochre; two small dark eyebrow spots. Eyes large, with dark brown irides. Ears dark, relatively large, and pointed. Fur above greenish-grey, sprinkled with silvery greyish-white hairs, especially along wing membranes; crown, occiput, area between eyes, and temporal region bright yellowish-ochre; mantle orange-buff, tinted ochraceous-rufous, shading to deep orange-brown on sides of neck and foreneck; chin and throat dark brown; cheeks pale yellow, with scattered whitish hairs; chest and belly ochraceous brown, with hints of buffy yellow; flanks similar or slightly paler; genitals contrastingly dark. Tibia furred on proximal half and sparsely haired on distal half. Wings blackish-brown, with claw on second digit.

Seychelles Flying Fox *Pteropus seychellensis* LC
Roussette des Seychelles

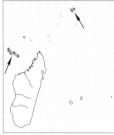

0–1000 m

FA 147–158 mm, **W** 370–390 g.
Primary and secondary tropical moist forest, and coral rag forest. Roosts in trees.
Head fox-like; muzzle long and tapering, dark brown, clearly contrasting with yellow fur on forehead. Ears naked and pointed; dark brown, without conspicuous basal ear patches. Fur of back blackish-brown (exceptionally with scattered pale grey hairs), with striking yellow, pale gold or brownish-yellow mantle; crown golden yellow to brownish-yellow; collar golden yellow to rusty yellow; chin and throat dark brown, turning to bright orange, rusty yellow or bright rusty brown on chest, and dark brown with pale yellow wash on belly and flanks. Wings blackish-brown, and attached to second toe; uropatagium relatively well developed.

Greater Mascarene Flying Fox *Pteropus niger* EN
Roussette des Mascareignes

FA 143–171 mm, **W** 380–540 g.
Forested areas, mainly in mountain ranges with restricted access.
Snout blackish; head yellowish to yellowish-brown, dark russet-brown on crown. Eyes large, with brown irides. Ears small and pointed, almost hidden in fur; outer margin clearly concave and without conspicuous basal ear patches. Nape dark cinnamon-rufous, becoming chestnut and then dark russet-brown on mantle, with dark brown mid-back area (spinal track); and buffy sides of back and rump; below dark reddish-brown, darker on throat; anal region buff to ochraceous buff, as is thickly furred tibia. Wings blackish-brown; uropatagium narrow, central part hidden by fur.

Paulian's Trident Bat *Paratriaenops pauliani* `DD`
Triaenops de Paulian

FA 41·4–45·1 mm, **W** 6·5 g (single individual). Dry shrubland and coconut plantations. Reportedly confined to Picard Island. Fur pale to dull grey or brownish-grey, slightly darker above than below. Noseleaf large, rounded and relatively broad, with strap-like, longitudinal and anteriorly shallowly bifurcated projection across anterior part of anterior leaf, above anterior medial emargination; three tall pointed projections on posterior part of posterior leaf, with short, laterally flattened, slightly upward-directed projection in medial position; total width of three posterior projections almost equals entire width of posterior leaf; posterior leaf scalloped by numerous small, similar-sized cells, arranged in two transversal rows, separated from each other by fleshy septa, except central pair in posterior row, which are separated by incomplete septum; tall posterior projections not emarginated at bases; lateral two projections slightly curved medially, and medial projection is markedly broader at its base than lateral projections; no lateral supplementary leaflets, but thickened ridge beneath margin of anterior leaf. Ears large and pointed; anterior margin evenly rounded.

Seychelles Sheath-tailed Bat *Coleura seychellensis* `CR`
Emballonure des Seychelles

FA 51·9–56·4 mm, **W** 10·2–11·1 g. Coastal boulder fields, native palm woodland dominated by *Nephrosperma*, and marsh habitats. Fur of upperparts and chest reddish-brown; underparts slightly paler. Eyes large and conspicuous. Flight membranes reddish-brown. Female larger than male.

134

FREE-TAILED BATS Molossidae

Réunion Goblin Bat *Mormopterus francoismoutoui* LC
Molosse de La Réunion

0–2500 m

FA 38–42 mm, **W** 5–7·2 g. Variety of non-forested habitats, both natural and man-modified. Slightly flattened head, no facial ornamentation; tail protrudes beyond hind margin of uropatagium. Fur above short, uniformly dark brown; similar below becoming paler on belly. Ears small, erect, subtriangular, without complex folds, and joined together by narrow flap of skin, with slight sickle-shaped emargination below tips; tragus small but not concealed by antitragus. Adult male has distinct throat gland, absent in female. Upper lips have several wrinkles, a few spoon-hairs, and many fine hairs. Wings and uropatagium dark brown. Hindclaws have fine hairs and many stout bristles.

Mauritian Goblin Bat *Mormopterus acetabulosus* EN
Molosse de Port-Louis

FA 38–43 mm, **W** 6–8·2 g. Scrubland, woodland and agricultural areas. Roosts in caves. Slightly flattened head, no facial ornamentation; tail protrudes beyond hind margin of uropatagium. Fur short, above uniformly dark brown; paler on belly. Ears small, erect, subtriangular, without complex folds, and separated at bases, with distinct sickle-shaped emargination below tips; tragus small but not concealed by antitragus. Adult male has distinct throat gland, absent in female. Upper lips have several deep wrinkles, few spoon-hairs, and many fine hairs. Wings and uropatagium dark brown. Hindclaws have fine hairs and many stout bristles.

Seychelles Free-tailed Bat *Chaerephon pusillus* VU
Tadaride des Seychelles

0–410 m

FA 36–39 mm, **W** 5–12 g. Dry scrub, dry woodland and anthropogenic habitats. Fur short, reddish-brown above, medium brown below; lacks white flank-stripe of African *C. pumilus*. Upper lip has 5–7+ well-defined wrinkles on each side and many spoon-hairs. Ears medium brown and relatively small, containing interaural pouch which houses erectile crest in male; antitragus somewhat rounded and arch-shaped, with slight anterior elongation. Wings medium brown; uropatagium dark brown.

VESPER BATS Vespertilionidae

Réunion House Bat *Scotophilus borbonicus* DD
Scotophile de Bourbon

FA 51 mm (one specimen).
No information on habitat.
Fur reddish-brown above, dull whitish below. Known only from a single old specimen in very poor condition. Recent genetic work suggests type specimen may be synonymous with *S. trujilloi*
of mainland Tanzania, and provenance of *borbonicus* type specimen is now questioned. A specimen from south-west Madagascar, previously suggested to refer to *borbonicus*, is not compatible with *S. trujilloi*, and may represent an undescribed species. Acoustic recordings suggest Réunion may nonetheless harbour a species of *Scotophilus*.

Anjouan Myotis *Myotis anjouanensis* DD
Murin d'Anjouan

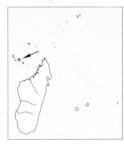

FA 43 mm, **W** 6-6 g.
Recorded in an area surrounded by heavily disturbed forest and agricultural plots.
Similar to *M. goudotii* (see page 109) but larger, with fur above dark reddish-brown.

Introduced species

Mammals introduced to Madagascar and neighbouring island groups.

	Madagascar	Comoros[a]	Seychelles	Réunion	Mauritius[b]
Tenrec ecaudatus[1]	n	i	i	i	i
Eulemur fulvus[2]	n	i			
Eulemur mongoz[3]	n	i			
Macaca fascicularis					i
Oryctolagus cuniculus			i		i
Lepus nigricollis		i	i	i	i
Rattus norvegicus	i	i	i	i	i
Rattus rattus	i	i	i	i	i
Mus musculus	i	i	i	i	i
Suncus etruscus	i				
Suncus murinus	i	i		i	i
Rusa timorensis					i
Potamochoerus larvatus	i				
Viverricula indica	i				
Urva auropunctata		i			i

n = natural distribution, i = introduced
[a] = including Mayotte, [b] = with Rodrigues
[1] see page 27; [2] see page 65; [3] see page 70

OLD WORLD MONKEYS Cercopithecidae

Long-tailed Macaque *Macaca fascicularis*
Macaque crabier

HB 31·5–63 cm, **T** 31·5–71·5 cm, **W** 2·4–12 kg
(male larger than female).
Seashore, mangrove forest, riverbanks
and swamp forest; often near humans, in
fields, gardens and temple precincts.
Golden brown above, whitish below;
crown hairs typically darker, directed backwards
and outwards, often forming small central crest;
cheek whiskers usually sweep upwards; long tail
progressively paler towards tip.

Introduced to Mauritius (0–2000 m).

HARES AND RABBITS Leporidae

European Rabbit *Oryctolagus cuniculus*
Lapin de garenne

HB 360–380 mm, **T** 65–70 mm, **W** 1·5–3 kg.
Wide variety of habitats, but prefers areas of short grass
on dry and loosely compacted soils, with secure refuge
available in thickets, near open feeding grounds.
Fur above and on head pale brown and slightly flecked with
black and buff; below white, with some pale ginger-buff. Ears
lack black tips. Tail short; dark brown above, white below.

Introduced to Seychelles and Mauritius (0–1500 m).

Indian Hare *Lepus nigricollis*
Lièvre à col noir

HB 330–530 mm, **T** 10–90 mm, **W** 1·8–3·6 kg.
Open desert with scattered shrubs, thick jungle with
some open clearings, grassland, scrub and cultivated
plains.
Rufous-brown mixed with black above, throat and belly
white; neck patch varies from black to greyish; legs and chest
rufous.

Introduced to Comoros, Seychelles, Réunion and Mauritius.

TRUE MICE AND RATS, GERBILS AND RELATIVES Muridae

Brown Rat *Rattus norvegicus*
Rat brun

HB 160–290 mm, **T** 122–
250 mm, **W** 195–540 g.
Mostly commensal with
humans; found in very
wide range of man-made habitats.
Introduced worldwide.
Larger and more robust than *R. rattus*, with shorter, hairier ears. Fur long, shaggy and coarse; above
dirty greyish-brown to dark brown, paler along sides, below white to greyish-white. Tail c. 80–97% of
head–body length; indistinctly bicoloured.

Introduced to Madagascar, Comoros, Seychelles, Réunion and Mauritius.

Roof Rat *Rattus rattus*
Rat noir

HB 116–260 mm, **T** 120–260 mm,
W 85–300 g.
Originally temperate montane, and
tropical and subtropical evergreen forest;
now generally close to human habitation, both rural and urban, in and around
cultivation and cities. Introduced worldwide.
Fur sleek yet coarse, fairly short, shiny and covered with longer dark guard hairs; above black to
greyish-brown, below paler but not sharply demarcated. Ears longish, almost naked. Tail 95–120% of
head–body length; naked; unicoloured.

Introduced to Madagascar, Comoros, Seychelles, Réunion and Mauritius (0–2000 m).

House Mouse *Mus musculus*
Souris domestique

HB 70–103 mm, **T** 67–104 mm, **W** 12–39 g.
Mostly commensal with humans; found in a
very wide range of man-made habitats. Introduced
worldwide.
Uniform greyish-brown above, paler below. Tail as long as head–body length.

Introduced to Madagascar, Comoros, Seychelles, Réunion and Mauritius.

SHREWS Soricidae

Etruscan Shrew *Suncus etruscus*
Pachyure étrusque

HB 33–50 mm, **T** 21–30 mm, **W** 1·2–2·7 g.
Shrub thickets, gardens and riparian forest or
woodland associated with fluvial and floodplain areas in arid climates; much less common in dry
steppe and semi-desert, and avoids wet habitats; sometimes in buildings.
One of the smallest living mammals. Fur short and soft; above smoky grey not well demarcated from
silvery grey underparts. Tail usually longer than 60% of head–body length; weakly bicoloured.

Introduced to Madagascar.

Asian House Shrew *Suncus murinus*
Pachyure musqué

HB 90–160 mm, **T** 45–110 mm,
W 23·5–147·3 g.
Mostly commensal with humans, occurring near
villages, towns and cities, in various habitats including
agriculture, gardens, buildings and drains; sometimes
found in forest, scrubland and grassland, and on riverbanks.
Fur short, fine and dense; colour varies individually and geographically, from greyish-white or
greyish-brown to blackish-grey. Eyes very small. Tail relatively short and very thick at base, tapering to
fine point; covered in long and short silvery white hairs.

Introduced to Madagascar, Comoros, Réunion and Mauritius.

Javan Deer *Rusa timorensis*
Cerf de Timor

HB 140–180 cm, **T** 25 cm,
W 50–135 kg (male larger than female).
Originally grassland, but has adapted to
forest, shrubland and marshes.
Medium-sized deer with relatively long.
narrow tail; fur dark brown to grey-brown
above, paler below. Male has relatively
slender antlers (50–80 cm long), with
brow tine pointing forwards and trez
tine in median position; conspicuous neck
mane. Female paler. Newborn fawn unspotted.

Introduced to Mauritius (0–600 m).

Bushpig *Potamochoerus larvatus*
Potamochère du Cap

HB 100–150 cm, **T** 30–40 cm,
W 50–115 kg.
Wide range of forested and
woodland habitats, preferring valley
bottoms with soft soil and dense
vegetation.
Compact body with short legs,
rounded back and elongated snout.
Fur colour very variable, blond or
russet to dark brown or nearly black.
Head generally paler, with white face
markings. Body hairs long and sparse but elongated
from forehead to tail, forming white or greyish dorsal
crest. Tail long and tufted. Adult male has bony ridges
and calluses on muzzle. Upper tusks very small, but lower
tusks sizeable and razor-sharp.

Introduced to Madagascar (0–2500 m).

142

CIVETS, GENETS AND OYANS Viverridae

Small Indian Civet *Viverricula indica*
Civette indienne

HB 48·5–68 cm,
T 30–43 cm,
W 2–4 kg.
Various forest
types, as well as bamboo,
scrubland, grassland and
riparian habitat; also near
plantations and human
settlements.
Small terrestrial civet,

with no erectile dorsal crest; muzzle short, ears set close on forecrown. Coat grey to tawny or brown,
covered in small brown or black spots on flanks, which tend to run as 3–5 longitudinal lines down
back. Feet dark brown to black. Tail has 6–9 dark rings and white tip.

Introduced to Madagascar (0–1200 m).

MONGOOSES Herpestidae

Small Indian Mongoose *Urva auropunctata*
Mangouste tachetée

HB 25–37 cm, **T** 19·2–29 cm, **W** 305–662 g.
Forest, scrub and open habitats; also
close to human habitation. On
Mauritius, especially riparian and
dense forest, as well as woodland
and scrub.
Slender body and short legs. Fur buff to
rufous or dark yellowish-grey; hairs have white
and dark rings, giving grizzled appearance.

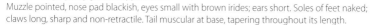

Muzzle pointed, nose pad blackish, eyes small with brown irides; ears short. Soles of feet naked;
claws long, sharp and non-retractile. Tail muscular at base, tapering throughout its length.

Introduced to Comoros and Mauritius (0–2100 m).

Where to watch mammals in Madagascar

When planning a visit to a different region, any keen mammal watcher wants to know where some of the most spectacular, unusual and rare species can most easily be searched out and seen. To facilitate this, on the following pages we provide a selective table of 52 of the best sites for watching mammals in Madagascar.

Each site in the table is named, and its current official protection status is given; a few of the sites listed currently lack any formal protection. Each site has also been given a number in the table, and this can be used to discover its location by consulting the map on page 157.

The second column states the ecosystem in which the site occurs. For a generalized idea of Madagascar's main vegetation zones see the map on page 17.

The third column presents a selection of the most notable mammal species that can be seen at each site. *Dark green* indicates that the site is one of the best for seeing the species in question, although it may also be seen at other sites in the table, and also elsewhere, at sites not covered in the table. *Pale blue* indicates that this is the only site in the table where the species can be seen, although once again it may also occur at other sites not included in the table.

Please note that in a few cases we are not yet certain which species of the genus indicated is present at a certain site. In such cases, we merely list the genus name with "sp.", for example "*Lepilemur* sp."

The fourth column deals with the relative accessibility of the site. "Easy" sites can be reached with little difficulty, and have adequate to excellent accommodation; they are on the normal tourist circuit. "Medium" sites require more effort in terms of logistics, and have only minimal accommodation or camping facilities. "Difficult" sites are much harder to reach, usually have little or nothing in terms of accommodation, and can also present security risks; they are generally only for specialists with considerable travel experience in Madagascar.

The fifth and final column simply states the region within which the site is located.

Immediately following the table, on page 157, is a relief map showing the approximate locality of each of the sites. The numbers on the map correspond to the sites, which are listed on the facing page.

Site	Ecosystem
1 Montagne des Français *Paysage Harmonieux Protégé*	Dry deciduous forest
2 Montagne d'Ambre National Park	Medium-altitude moist evergreen forest
3 Analamerana Special Reserve	Dry deciduous forest
4 Loky Manambato/Daraina *Paysage Harmonieux Protégé*	Medium-altitude moist evergreen forest, and moist semi-deciduous forest
5 Andriafiamena Andavakoera *Paysage Harmonieux Protégé*	Moist semi-deciduous forest
6 Ankarana Special Reserve	Humid semi-deciduous forest
7 Nosy Be	Marine
8 Lokobe National Park	Lowland moist evergreen forest
9 Nosy Komba No legal protection status	Lowland moist evergreen forest
10 Ampasindava *Paysage Harmonieux Protégé*	Lowland moist evergreen forest
11 Manongarivo Special Reserve	Lowland, medium- and high-altitude moist evergreen forest
12 Sahamalaza-Îles Radama National Park	Humid semi-deciduous forest
13 Bemanevika *Paysage Harmonieux Protégé*	Medium-altitude moist evergreen forest
14 Marojejy National Park	Lowland, medium- and high-altitude moist fore

able mammal species present at site	Accessibility	Region
gale dobsoni · *Paratriaenops auritus* · *Lepilemur septentrionalis* *ocebus tavaratra* · *Eulemur coronatus* · *Daubentonia madagascariensis*	Easy	North
ec ecaudatus · *Nesogale talazaci* · *Macronycteris commersonii* *eres goudotii* · *Galidia elegans* · *Cheirogaleus andysabini* *ocebus arnholdi* · *Phaner electromontis* · *Eulemur coronatus* *nur sanfordi* · *Lepilemur ankaranensis* · *Daubentonia madagascariensis*	Easy	North
gale brevicaudata · *Eliurus carletoni* · *Paratriaenops auritus* *rogaleus shethi* · *Microcebus tavaratra* · *Lepilemur ankaranensis* *er electromontis* · *Eulemur coronatus* · *Eulemur sanfordi* *lemur occidentalis* · *Propithecus perrieri* · *Daubentonia madagascariensis*	Medium	North
r setosus · *Microgale fotsifotsy* · *Paratriaenops auritus* *rogaleus shethi* · *Microcebus tavaratra* · *Microcebus arnholdi* *er electromontis* · *Lepilemur milanoii* · *Eulemur coronatus* *nur sanfordi* · *Propithecus tattersalli* · *Daubentonia madagascariensis*	Easy	North
c ecaudatus · *Eliurus carletoni* · *Paratriaenops auritus* · *Galidia elegans* *ogaleus shethi* · *Microcebus tavaratra* · *Phaner electromontis* *emur ankaranensis* · *Lepilemur milanoii* · *Eulemur coronatus* *nur sanfordi* · *Hapalemur occidentalis* · *Propithecus perrieri* *entonia madagascariensis*	Easy	North
riaenops auritus · *Coleura kibomalandy* · *Chaerephon jobimena* *ttus madagascariensis* · *Cryptoprocta ferox* · *Galidia elegans* *ogaleus shethi* · *Microcebus tavaratra* · *Phaner electromontis* *emur ankaranensis* · *Eulemur coronatus* · *Eulemur sanfordi* *Pemur occidentalis* · *Daubentonia madagascariensis*	Easy	North
ptera novaeangliae · *Balaenoptera omurai*	Easy	North
us rufus · *Rousettus madagascariensis* · *Paremballonura tiavato* *cebus mamiratra* · *Lepilemur tymerlachsoni* · *Eulemur macaco*	Easy	North
ur macaco	Easy	North
oterus aelleni · *Fossa fossana* · *Microcebus sambiranensis* *zaza* · *Phaner parienti* · *Lepilemur mittermeieri* · *Eulemur fulvus* *ur macaco* · *Hapalemur occidentalis* · *Avahi unicolor* *entonia madagascariensis*	Difficult	North
gale majori · *Eliurus grandidieri* · *Eliurus ellermani* · *Eupleres goudotii* *galeus crossleyi* · *Microcebus sambiranensis* · *Mirza zaza* *r parienti* · *Lepilemur dorsalis* · *Eulemur fulvus* · *Eulemur macaco* *ur rubriventer* · *Hapalemur occidentalis* · *Avahi unicolor* *ntonia madagascariensis*	Difficult	North
ecaudatus · *Scotophilus robustus* · *Cryptoprocta ferox* *ebus sambiranensis* · *Mirza zaza* · *Cheirogaleus medius* *ur flavifrons* · *Eulemur macaco* · *Hapalemur occidentalis* *nur sahamalaza* · *Daubentonia madagascariensis*	Medium	North
ale jobihely · *Brachytarsomys villosa* · *Miniopterus ambohitrensis* *ous trichotis* · *Cheirogaleus sp.* · *Microcebus mittermeieri* *nur sp.* · *Avahi occidentalis* · *Eulemur fulvus* · *Hapalemur occidentalis*	Difficult	North
ale gymnorhyncha · *Microgale thomasi* · *Brachytarsomys albicauda* *o gymnocaudus* · *Coleura kibomalandy* · *Allocebus trichotis* *ebus mittermeieri* · *Phaner furcifer* · *Cheirogaleus crossleyi* *galeus major* · *Cheirogaleus sibreei* · *Lepilemur seali* *r rubriventer* · *Eulemur albifrons* · *Hapalemur occidentalis* *aniger* · *Propithecus candidus* · *Daubentonia madagascariensis*	Medium	North-east

Site	Ecosystem
15 **Anjanaharibe-Sud** Special Reserve	Lowland and medium-altitude moist evergreen fo
16 **Makira** Natural Park	Lowland and medium-altitude moist forest
17 **Masoala** National Park	Lowland, medium- and high-altitude moist forest and marine
18 **Nosy Mangabe** National Park	Lowland moist evergreen forest, and marine
19 **Mananara-Nord** National Park (including Île Roger)	Lowland moist evergreen forest
20 **Île Sainte Marie**	Lowland moist evergreen forest, and marine
21 **Lake Alaotra** *Paysage Harmonieux Protégé*	Freshwater
22 **Zahamena** National Park	Lowland and medium-altitude moist evergreen
23 **Anjozorobe-Angavo** *Paysage Harmonieux Protégé*	Medium-altitude moist evergreen forest
24 **Betampona** Strict Nature Reserve	Lowland moist evergreen forest
25 **Mantadia** National Park	Medium-altitude moist evergreen forest

able mammal species present at site	Accessibility	Region
rogale dryas · Microgale monticola · Brachytarsomys albicauda :hytarsomys villosa · Voalavo gymnocaudus · Eidolon dupreanum dia elegans · Allocebus trichotis · Cheirogaleus major ocebus mittermeieri · Phaner furcifer · Lepilemur seali · Eulemur albifrons mur rubriventer · Hapalemur occidentalis · Avahi laniger · Indri indri ithecus candidus · Daubentonia madagascariensis	Medium	North-east
ogale dryas · Microgale mergulus · Microgale monticola hytarsomys albicauda · Miniopterus gleni · Salanoia concolor ebus trichotis · Cheirogaleus major · Microcebus macarthurii ocebus mittermeieri · Phaner furcifer · Lepilemur seali · Eulemur albifrons mur fulvus · Eulemur rubriventer · Hapalemur occidentalis cia rubra · Varecia variegata subcincta · Avahi laniger · Indri indri ithecus candidus · Daubentonia madagascariensis	Difficult	North-east
ogale principula · Nesomys audeberti · Myotis goudotii lictis fasciata · Salanoia concolor · Allocebus trichotis rogaleus major · Phaner furcifer · Lepilemur scottorum nur albifrons · Eulemur fulvus · Hapalemur occidentalis · Varecia rubra i mooreorum · Daubentonia madagascariensis · Megaptera novaeangliae	Medium	North-east
pus rufus · Miniopteris gleni · Cheirogaleus major · Microcebus sp. nur albifrons · Varecia variegata subcincta (introduced) entonia madagascariensis (introduced) · Megaptera novaeangliae	Medium	North-east
centetes semispinosus · Eliurus grandidieri · Pteropus rufus oia concolor · Galidia elegans · Allocebus trichotis ogaleus major · Phaner furcifer · Lepilemur hollandorum nur albifrons · Eulemur rubriventer · Hapalemur occidentalis ia variegata subcincta · Avahi laniger · Indri indri · Propithecus diadema entonia madagascariensis (Île Roger–introduced)	Difficult	North-east
ptera novaeangliae · Microcebus boraha	Easy	East
yuromys betsileoensis · Laephotis matroka · Chaerephon atsinanana oia concolor · Hapalemur alaotrensis	Easy	East
gale parvula · Brachytarsomys albicauda · Allocebus trichotis ogaleus crossleyi · Microcebus simmonsi · Phaner furcifer mur mustelinus · Eulemur fulvus · Eulemur rubriventer lemur griseus griseus · Prolemur simus · Varecia variegata variegata laniger · Indri indri · Propithecus diadema entonia madagascariensis	Difficult	East
gale cowani · Oryzorictes hova · Brachytarsomys albicauda vo antsahabensis · Laephotis robertsi · Cheirogaleus crossleyi ogaleus sibreei · Microcebus lehilahytsara · Lepilemur mustelinus ur fulvus · Hapalemur griseus griseus · Avahi laniger hecus diadema · Indri indri	Easy	East
setosus · Eliurus petteri · Cheirogaleus major · Microcebus simmonsi r furcifer · Lepilemur mustelinus · Eulemur albifrons emur griseus griseus · Varecia variegata variegata · Avahi laniger dri · Propithecus diadema · Daubentonia madagascariensis	Medium	East
ale soricoides · Microgale drouhardi · Eliurus petteri otis robertsi · Fossa fossana · Allocebus trichotis galeus crossleyi · Microcebus lehilahytsara · Lepilemur mustelinus ur fulvus · Eulemur rubriventer · Hapalemur griseus griseus a variegata editorum · Avahi laniger · Indri indri hecus diadema · Daubentonia madagascariensis	Easy	East

Site	Ecosystem
26 **Andasibe/Analamazaotra/Périnet** National Park Including the Association des Guides d'Andasibe VOI Community Reserve and Association Mitsinjo Reserve	Medium-altitude moist evergreen forest
27 **Torotorofotsy** Protected Area	Medium-altitude moist evergreen forest
28 **Maromizaha** *Réserve de Ressources Naturelles*	Medium-altitude moist evergreen forest
29 **Mangabe–Ranomena–Sahasarotra** *Réserve de Ressources Naturelles*	Medium-altitude moist evergreen forest
30 **Ranomafana** National Park (Including Vohiparara)	Medium-altitude moist evergreen forest
31 **Kianjavato** No legal protection status	Lowland and medium-altitude moist evergreen fo
32 **Marolambo** National Park	Medium-altitude moist evergreen forest
33 **Andringitra** National Park	Medium- and high-altitude moist evergreen fore
34 **Manombo** Special Reserve	Lowland moist evergreen forest
35 **Kalambatritra** Special Reserve	Medium-altitude moist evergreen forest
36 **Andohahela** National Park (Parcel I)	Lowland, medium- and high-altitude moist ever forest
37 **Andohahela** National Park (Parcels II & III)	Dry spiny thicket (Parcel II) and transition betwee spiny thicket and moist evergreen forest (Parcel

able mammal species present at site	Accessibility	Region
ogale cowani · Tenrec ecaudatus · Hemicentetes semispinosus us petteri · Brachytarsomys albicauda · Pipistrellus raceyi dia elegans · Allocebus trichotis · Cheirogaleus crossleyi ocebus lehilahytsara · Lepilemur mustelinus · Eulemur fulvus mur rubriventer · Hapalemur griseus griseus · Avahi laniger · Indri indri bentonia madagascariensis	Easy	East
mys audeberti · Eliurus tanala · Eupleres goudotii · Allocebus trichotis rogaleus crossleyi · Microcebus lehilahytsara · Lepilemur mustelinus alemur griseus griseus · Prolemur simus · Eulemur fulvus mur rubriventer · Varecia variegata editorum · Avahi laniger thecus diadema · Indri indri · Daubentonia madagascariensis	Medium	East
ogale gracilis · Microgale longicaudata · Eliurus grandidieri ettus madagascariensis · Fossa fossana · Allocebus trichotis rogaleus crossleyi · Microcebus lehilahytsara · Lepilemur mustelinus lemur griseus griseus · Eulemur fulvus · Eulemur rubriventer cia variegata editorum · Avahi laniger · Propithecus diadema indri · Daubentonia madagascariensis	Easy	East
s webbi · Microcebus lehilahytsara · Cheirogaleus major mur fulvus · Avahi laniger · Propithecus diadema · Indri indri entonia madagascariensis	Medium	East
gale mergulus · Brachytarsomys albicauda · Monticolomys koopmani fossana · Galidia elegans · Cheirogaleus crossleyi ogaleus grovesi · Cheirogaleus sibreei · Microcebus rufus mur microdon · Eulemur rubriventer · Eulemur rufifrons lemur aureus · Hapalemur griseus ranomafanensis · Prolemur simus ia variegata editorum · Avahi peyrierasi · Propithecus edwardsi entonia madagascariensis	Easy	East
ogaleus major · Microcebus jollyae · Eulemur rufifrons mur simus · Varecia variegata editorum entonia madagascariensis	Easy	East
rictes hova · Microgale parvula · Eliurus penicillatus colomys koopmani · Miniopterus sororculus · Cheirogaleus medius cebus marohita · Lepilemur betsileo · Eulemur rubriventer ur rufifrons · Hapalemur griseus ranomafanensis · Prolemur simus a variegata editorum · Avahi laniger · Propithecus edwardsi	Difficult	East
entetes nigriceps · Microgale mergulus · Oryzorictes tetradactylus colomys koopmani · Cheirogaleus grovesi · Microcebus rufus nur microdon · Eulemur fulvus · Eulemur rubriventer emur aureus · Hapalemur griseus ranomafanensis · Lemur catta nur simus · Varecia variegata editorum · Avahi peyrierasi hecus edwardsi	Medium	East
ys audeberti · Pteropus rufus · Lepilemur jamesorum ur cinereiceps · Hapalemur meridionalis · Varecia variegata editorum ramanantsoavani · Daubentonia madagascariensis	Easy	East
colomys koopmani · Cheirogaleus lavasoensis · Lepilemur wrightae ur collaris · Hapalemur meridionalis · Lemur catta · Avahi meridionalis ntionia madagascariensis	Difficult	East
tarsomys albicauda · Monticolomys koopmani · Cheirogaleus major mur fleuretae · Eulemur collaris · Hapalemur meridionalis meridionalis · Daubentonia madagascariensis	Medium	South-east
galeus medius · Microcebus griseorufus · Microcebus murinus pallescens · Lepilemur leucopus · Lemur catta ecus verreauxi	Easy	South-east

Site	Ecosystem
38 **Mandena** *Paysage Harmonieux Protégé*	Littoral forest on sand
39 **Sainte Luce (Ambato Atsinanana)** No legal protection status	Littoral forest on sand
40 **Petriky** *Paysage Harmonieux Protégé*	Littoral forest on sand
41 **Berenty** Private Reserve	Dry spiny thicket and riparian forest
42 **Bongolava** *Paysage Harmonieux Protégé*	Dry deciduous forest
43 **Baie de Baly** National Park	Dry deciduous forest
44 **Antrema** *Réserve de Ressources Naturelles*	Dry deciduous forest
45 **Ankarafantsika/Ampijoroa** National Park	Dry deciduous forest
46 **Bemaraha** National Park	Dry deciduous forest
47 **Kirindy/Menabe Antimena** *Paysage Harmonieux Protégé* (including CNFEREF Research Station and Camp Amoureux)	Dry deciduous forest
48 **Makay** No legal protection status	Dry deciduous forest
49 **Isalo** National Park	Riparian forest
50 **Zombitse-Vohibasia** National Park	Dry deciduous forest
51 **Beza-Mahafaly** Special Reserve	Dry spiny thicket
52 **Tsimanampetsotse** National Park	Dry spiny thicket

able mammal species present at site	Accessibility	Region
opterus petersoni · Cryptoprocta ferox · Cheirogaleus thomasi rogaleus major · Microcebus ganzhorni · Eulemur collaris alemur meridionalis · Avahi meridionalis	Easy	South-east
rogaleus thomasi · Microcebus tanosi · Eulemur collaris ai meridionalis	Easy	South-east
nops telfairi · Macrotarsomys bastardi · Scotophilus robustus rogaleus thomasi · Microcebus ganzhorni · Microcebus griseorufus ur catta · Propithecus verreauxi	Easy	South-east
opus rufus · Lepilemur leucopus · Microcebus murinus ocebus griseorufus · Lemur catta · Eulemur collaris/rufifrons hybrid ithecus verreauxi	Easy	South-east
us myoxinus · Microcebus bongolavensis · Lepilemur otto nur fulvus · Eulemur mongoz · Avahi occidentalis · Propithecus coquereli	Difficult	West
rogaleus medius · Microcebus myoxinus · Microcebus murinus emur sp. · Hapalemur griseus ranomafanensis · Eulemur rufus ithecus verreauxi	Medium	West
cebus murinus · Lepilemur aeeclis · Eulemur fulvus · Eulemur mongoz ithecus coronatus	Easy	West
gale brevicaudata · Macrotarsomys ingens · Cryptoprocta ferox ogaleus medius · Microcebus ravelobensis · Microcebus murinus emur edwardsi · Eulemur fulvus · Eulemur mongoz · Avahi occidentalis thecus coquereli	Easy	West
gale grandidieri · Nesomys lambertoni · Eliurus antsingy s tsingimbato · Scotophilus tandrefana · Cryptoprocta ferox ogaleus medius · Microcebus myoxinus · Mirza coquereli er pallescens · Lepilemur randrianasoloi · Eulemur rufus emur griseus ranomafanensis · Avahi cleesei · Propithecus deckenii entonia madagascariensis	Medium	West
gale nasoloi · Hypogeomys antimena · Cryptoprocta ferox otictis decemlineata · Neoromicia bemainty · Cheirogaleus medius cebus berthae · Microcebus murinus · Mirza coquereli er pallescens · Lepilemur ruficaudatus · Eulemur rufus hecus verreauxi	Easy	West
ebus murinus · Cheirogaleus medius · Mirza coquereli er pallescens · Lepilemur ruficaudatus · Hapalemur griseus ranomafanensis ur rufifrons · Propithecus verreauxi	Medium	West
s danieli · Chaerephon jobimena · Laephotis malagasyensis nycteris cryptovalorona · Cheirogaleus medius · Microcebus murinus coquereli · Lepilemur hubbardi · Eulemur rufifrons · Lemur catta hecus verreauxi	Easy	South-west
gale nasoloi · Chaerephon jobimena · Crypyptoprocta ferox galeus medius · Microcebus murinus · Mirza coquereli pallescens · Lepilemur hubbardi · Eulemur rufifrons catta · Propithecus verreauxi	Easy	South-west
ebus griseorufus · Lepilemur petteri · Lemur catta hecus verreauxi	Medium	South-west
nycteris cryptovalorona · Miniopterus griffithsi tis fasciata grandidieri · Microcebus griseorufus · Lepilemur petteri catta · Propithecus verreauxi	Medium	South-west

1. Montagne des Français
2. Montagne d'Ambre
3. Analamerana
4. Loky Manambato/Daraina
5. Andriafiamena Andavakoera
6. Ankarana
7. Nosy Be
8. Lokobe
9. Nosy Komba
10. Ampasindava
11. Manongarivo
12. Sahamalaza-Îles Radama
13. Bemanevika
14. Marojejy
15. Anjanaharibe-Sud
16. Makira
17. Masoala
18. Nosy Mangabe
19. Mananara-Nord
20. Île Sainte Marie
21. Lake Alaotra
22. Zahamena
23. Anjozorobe-Angavo
24. Betampona
25. Mantadia
26. Andasibe/Analamazaotra/Périnet

27. Torotorofotsy
28. Maromizaha
29. Mangabe–Ranomena–Sahasarotra
30. Ranomafana
31. Kianjavato
32. Marolambo
33. Andringitra
34. Manombo
35. Kalambatritra
36. Andohahela (Parcel I)
37. Andohahela (Parcels II & III)
38. Mandena
39. Sainte Luce (Ambato Atsinanana)
40. Petriky
41. Berenty
42. Bongolava
43. Baie de Baly
44. Antrema
45. Ankarafantsika/Ampijoroa
46. Bemaraha
47. Kirindy/Menabe Antimena
48. Makay
49. Isalo
50. Zombitse-Vohibasia
51. Beza-Mahafaly
52. Tsimanampetsotse

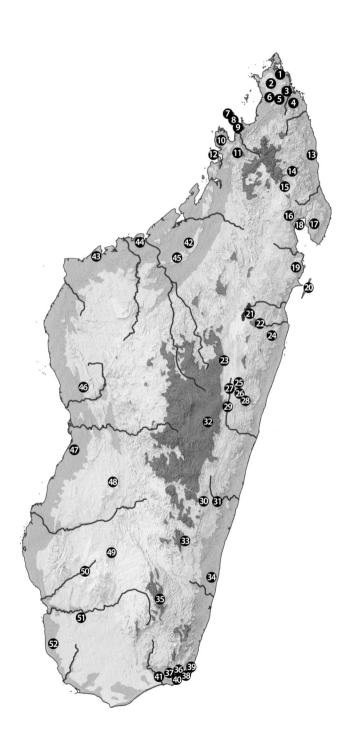

Checklist

			Status	Madagascar	Comoros[a]	Seychelles	Reunion	Mauritius[b]
TENRECS TENRECIDAE p. 27								
Lesser Hedgehog Tenrec	Petit Tenrec-hérisson	*Echinops telfairi*	LC	x				
Greater Hedgehog Tenrec	Grand Tenrec-hérisson	*Setifer setosus*	LC	x				
Tailless Tenrec	Tenrec commun	*Tenrec ecaudatus*	LC	x	i	i	i	i
Lowland Streaked Tenrec	Tenrec rayé	*Hemicentetes semispinosus*	LC	x				
Highland Streaked Tenrec	Tenrec à tête noire	*Hemicentetes nigriceps*	LC	x				
Large-eared Tenrec	Géogale	*Geogale aurita*	LC	x				
Hova Mole Tenrec	Oryzoricte taupe	*Oryzorictes hova*	LC	x				
Four-toed Mole Tenrec	Oryzoricte à quatre doigts	*Oryzorictes tetradactylus*	DD	x				
Dobson's Shrew Tenrec	Microgale de Dobson	*Nesogale dobsoni*	LC	x				
Talazac's Shrew Tenrec	Microgale de Talazac	*Nesogale talazaci*	LC	x				
Gracile Shrew Tenrec	Microgale gracile	*Microgale gracilis*	LC	x				
Thomas's Shrew Tenrec	Microgale de Thomas	*Microgale thomasi*	LC	x				
Dark Shrew Tenrec	Microgale du Tsaratanana	*Microgale jobihely*	EN	x				
Cowan's Shrew Tenrec	Microgale de Cowan	*Microgale cowani*	LC	x				
Dryad Shrew Tenrec	Microgale dryade	*Microgale dryas*	VU	x				
Naked-nosed Shrew Tenrec	Microgale à museau nu	*Microgale gymnorhyncha*	LC	x				
Nasolo's Shrew Tenrec	Microgale de Nasolo	*Microgale nasoloi*	VU	x				
Pale Shrew Tenrec	Microgale pâle	*Microgale fotsifotsy*	LC	x				
Shrew-toothed Shrew Tenrec	Microgale soriçoïde	*Microgale soricoides*	LC	x				
Short-tailed Shrew Tenrec	Microgale à queue courte	*Microgale brevicaudata*	LC	x				
Grandidier's Shrew Tenrec	Microgale de Grandidier	*Microgale grandidieri*	LC	x				
Drouhard's Shrew Tenrec	Microgale de Drouhard	*Microgale drouhardi*	LC	x				
Montane Shrew Tenrec	Microgale des montagnes	*Microgale monticola*	VU	x				
Taiva Shrew Tenrec	Microgale des Taivas	*Microgale taiva*	LC	x				
Web-footed Shrew Tenrec	Microgale plongeur	*Microgale mergulus*	VU	x				
Pygmy Shrew Tenrec	Microgale pygmée	*Microgale parvula*	LC	x				
Major's Long-tailed Shrew Tenrec	Microgale de Major	*Microgale majori*	LC	x				
Lesser Long-tailed Shrew Tenrec	Microgale à longue queue	*Microgale longicaudata*	LC	x				
Jenkins's Shrew Tenrec	Microgale de Jenkins	*Microgale jenkinsae*	EN	x				
Greater Long-tailed Shrew Tenrec	Grand Microgale	*Microgale principula*	LC	x				
Least Shrew Tenrec	Petit Microgale	*Microgale pusilla*	LC	x				
DUGONG DUGONGIDAE p. 37								
Dugong	Dugong	*Dugong dugon*	VU	x	x	x		
MOUSE, GIANT MOUSE, DWARF AND FORK-MARKED LEMURS CHEIROGALEIDAE p. 38								
Grey Mouse Lemur	Microcèbe murin	*Microcebus murinus*	LC	x				
Ganzhorn's Mouse Lemur	Microcèbe de Ganzhorn	*Microcebus ganzhorni*	EN	x				
Bemanasy Mouse Lemur	Microcèbe pionnier	*Microcebus manitatra*	CR	x				
Grey-brown Mouse Lemur	Microcèbe gris-roux	*Microcebus griseorufus*	LC	x				
Ambarijeby Mouse Lemur	Microcèbe de Danfoss	*Microcebus danfossi*	VU	x				
Bongolava Mouse Lemur	Microcèbe du Bongolava	*Microcebus bongolavensis*	EN	x				
Golden-brown Mouse Lemur	Microcèbe doré	*Microcebus ravelobensis*	VU	x				
Anjiahely Mouse Lemur	Microcèbe de MacArthur	*Microcebus macarthurii*	EN	x				
Jonah's Mouse Lemur	Microcèbe de Jonah	*Microcebus jonahi*	NE	x				
Marohita Mouse Lemur	Microcèbe de Marohita	*Microcebus marohita*	CR	x				
Gerp's Mouse Lemur	Microcèbe du Gerp	*Microcebus gerpi*	CR	x				
Tavaratra Mouse Lemur	Microcèbe du Nord	*Microcebus tavaratra*	VU	x				

IUCN Red List conservation status.
NE Not Evaluated DD Data Deficient LC Least Concern NT Near Threatened VU Vulnerable EN Endangered CR Critically Endangered

Presence.
x = natural distribution, i = introduced   [a] = including Mayotte, [b] = with Rodrigues

			Status	Madagascar	Comoros[a]	Seychelles	Réunion	Mauritius[b]
Tanosy Mouse Lemur	Microcèbe de Tanosy	*Microcebus tanosi*	EN	x				
Jolly's Mouse Lemur	Microcèbe de Jolly	*Microcebus jollyae*	EN	x				
Nosy Boraha Mouse Lemur	Microcèbe de Boraha	*Microcebus boraha*	DD	x				
Simmons's Mouse Lemur	Microcèbe de Simmons	*Microcebus simmonsi*	EN	x				
Nosy Be Mouse Lemur	Microcèbe de Claire	*Microcebus mamiratra*	EN	x				
Margot Marsh's Mouse Lemur	Microcèbe de Marsh	*Microcebus margotmarshae*	EN	x				
Sambirano Mouse Lemur	Microcèbe du Sambirano	*Microcebus sambiranensis*	EN	x				
Montagne d'Ambre Mouse Lemur	Microcèbe d'Arnhold	*Microcebus arnholdi*	VU	x				
Mittermeier's Mouse Lemur	Microcèbe de Mittermeier	*Microcebus mittermeieri*	EN	x				
Goodman's Mouse Lemur	Microcèbe de Goodman	*Microcebus lehilahytsara*	VU	x				
Madame Berthe's Mouse Lemur	Microcèbe de Berthe	*Microcebus berthae*	CR	x				
Peters's Mouse Lemur	Microcèbe pygmée	*Microcebus myoxinus*	VU	x				
Rufous Mouse Lemur	Microcèbe roux	*Microcebus rufus*	VU	x				
Coquerel's Giant Mouse Lemur	Microcèbe de Coquerel	*Mirza coquereli*	EN	x				
Northern Giant Mouse Lemur	Microcèbe zaza	*Mirza zaza*	VU	x				
Hairy-eared Dwarf Lemur	Allocèbe	*Allocebus trichotis*	EN	x				
Sibree's Dwarf Lemur	Chirogale de Sibree	*Cheirogaleus sibreei*	CR	x				
Ankarana Dwarf Lemur	Chirogale de Sheth	*Cheirogaleus shethi*	EN	x				
Thomas's Dwarf Lemur	Chirogale de Thomas	*Cheirogaleus thomasi*	EN	x				
Fat-tailed Dwarf Lemur	Petit Chirogale	*Cheirogaleus medius*	VU	x				
Greater Dwarf Lemur	Grand Chirogale	*Cheirogaleus major*	VU	x				
Sabin's Dwarf Lemur	Chirogale de Sabin	*Cheirogaleus andysabini*	EN	x				
Groves's Dwarf Lemur	Chirogale de Groves	*Cheirogaleus grovesi*	DD	x				
Lavasoa Dwarf Lemur	Chirogale du Lavasoa	*Cheirogaleus lavasoensis*	EN	x				
Crossley's Dwarf Lemur	Chirogale de Crossley	*Cheirogaleus crossleyi*	VU	x				
Masoala Fork-marked Lemur	Phaner à fourche	*Phaner furcifer*	EN	x				
Pale Fork-marked Lemur	Phaner pâle	*Phaner pallescens*	EN	x				
Sambirano Fork-marked Lemur	Phaner de Pariente	*Phaner parienti*	EN	x				
Montagne d'Ambre Fork-marked Lemur	Phaner de la Montagne d'Ambre	*Phaner electromontis*	EN	x				

SPORTIVE LEMURS LEPILEMURIDAE p. 52

			Status	Madagascar	Comoros[a]	Seychelles	Réunion	Mauritius[b]
Masoala Sportive Lemur	Lépilémur des Scott	*Lepilemur scottorum*	EN	x				
Mananara-Nord Sportive Lemur	Lépilémur des Holland	*Lepilemur hollandorum*	CR	x				
Seal's Sportive Lemur	Lépilémur de Seal	*Lepilemur seali*	VU	x				
Wright's Sportive Lemur	Lépilémur de Wright	*Lepilemur wrightae*	EN	x				
Andohahela Sportive Lemur	Lépilémur de Fleurette	*Lepilemur fleuretae*	EN	x				
Weasel Sportive Lemur	Lépilémur mustelin	*Lepilemur mustelinus*	VU	x				
Betsileo Sportive Lemur	Lépilémur du Betsileo	*Lepilemur betsileo*	EN	x				
Manombo Sportive Lemur	Lépilémur des James	*Lepilemur jamesorum*	CR	x				
White-footed Sportive Lemur	Lépilémur à pieds blancs	*Lepilemur leucopus*	EN	x				
Petter's Sportive Lemur	Lépilémur de Petter	*Lepilemur petteri*	EN	x				
Bemaraha Sportive Lemur	Lépilémur de Randrianasolo	*Lepilemur randrianasoloi*	EN	x				
Antafia Sportive Lemur	Lépilémur d'Antafia	*Lepilemur aeeclis*	EN	x				
Red-tailed Sportive Lemur	Lépilémur à queue rousse	*Lepilemur ruficaudatus*	CR	x				
Zombitse Sportive Lemur	Lépilémur de Hubbard	*Lepilemur hubbardi*	EN	x				
Small-toothed Sportive Lemur	Lépilémur à petites dents	*Lepilemur microdon*	EN	x				
Ambodimahabibo Sportive Lemur	Lépilémur d'Otto	*Lepilemur otto*	EN	x				
Anjiamangirana Sportive Lemur	Lépilémur des Grewcock	*Lepilemur grewcockorum*	CR	x				
Milne-Edwards's Sportive Lemur	Lépilémur de Milne-Edwards	*Lepilemur edwardsi*	EN	x				
Sahafary Sportive Lemur	Lépilémur septentrional	*Lepilemur septentrionalis*	CR	x				
Sahamalaza Sportive Lemur	Lépilémur de Sahamalaza	*Lepilemur sahamalaza*	CR	x				
Tsiombikibo Sportive Lemur	Lépilémur des Ahmanson	*Lepilemur ahmansonorum*	CR	x				
Gray's Sportive Lemur	Lépilémur à dos gris	*Lepilemur dorsalis*	EN	x				
Mittermeier's Sportive Lemur	Lépilémur de Mittermeier	*Lepilemur mittermeieri*	CR	x				
Nosy Be Sportive Lemur	Lépilémur de Nosy Be	*Lepilemur tymerlachsoni*	CR	x				

			Status	Madagascar	Comoros[a]	Seychelles	Réunion	Mauritius[b]
Daraina Sportive Lemur	Lépilémur de Daraina	*Lepilemur milanoii*	EN	x				
Ankarana Sportive Lemur	Lépilémur de l'Ankarana	*Lepilemur ankaranensis*	EN	x				

BAMBOO, TRUE AND RUFFED LEMURS LEMURIDAE p. 61

			Status	Madagascar	Comoros[a]	Seychelles	Réunion	Mauritius[b]
Grey Bamboo Lemur	Hapalémur gris	*Hapalemur griseus*	VU	x				
Southern Bamboo Lemur	Hapalémur méridional	*Hapalemur meridionalis*	VU	x				
Northern Bamboo Lemur	Hapalémur occidental	*Hapalemur occidentalis*	VU	x				
Lac Alaotra Bamboo Lemur	Hapalémur de l'Alaotra	*Hapalemur alaotrensis*	CR	x				
Golden Bamboo Lemur	Hapalémur doré	*Hapalemur aureus*	CR	x				
Greater Bamboo Lemur	Lémur à nez large	*Prolemur simus*	CR	x				
Ring-tailed Lemur	Lémur catta	*Lemur catta*	EN	x				
Brown Lemur	Lémur brun	*Eulemur fulvus*	VU	x			i	
Rufous Brown Lemur	Lémur roux	*Eulemur rufus*	VU	x				
Red-fronted Brown Lemur	Lémur à front roux	*Eulemur rufifrons*	VU	x				
White-fronted Brown Lemur	Lémur à front blanc	*Eulemur albifrons*	VU	x				
Sanford's Brown Lemur	Lémur de Sanford	*Eulemur sanfordi*	EN	x				
White-collared Brown Lemur	Lémur à collier blanc	*Eulemur cinereiceps*	CR	x				
Red-collared Brown Lemur	Lémur à collier roux	*Eulemur collaris*	EN	x				
Black Lemur	Lémur noir	*Eulemur macaco*	EN	x				
Blue-eyed Black Lemur	Lémur aux yeux turquoise	*Eulemur flavifrons*	CR	x				
Crowned Lemur	Lémur couronné	*Eulemur coronatus*	EN	x				
Red-bellied Lemur	Lémur à ventre roux	*Eulemur rubriventer*	VU	x				
Mongoose Lemur	Lémur mongoz	*Eulemur mongoz*	CR	x			i	
Black-and-white Ruffed Lemur	Vari noir et blanc	*Varecia variegata*	CR	x				
Red Ruffed Lemur	Vari roux	*Varecia rubra*	CR	x				

WOOLLY LEMURS, SIFAKAS AND INDRI INDRIIDAE p. 73

			Status	Madagascar	Comoros[a]	Seychelles	Réunion	Mauritius[b]
Eastern Woolly Lemur	Avahi laineux	*Avahi laniger*	VU	x				
Masoala Woolly Lemur	Avahi des Moore	*Avahi mooreorum*	EN	x				
Peyriéras's Woolly Lemur	Avahi de Peyriéras	*Avahi peyrierasi*	VU	x				
Betsileo Woolly Lemur	Avahi du Betsileo	*Avahi betsileo*	EN	x				
Manombo Woolly Lemur	Avahi de Manombo	*Avahi ramanantsoavani*	VU	x				
Southern Woolly Lemur	Avahi méridional	*Avahi meridionalis*	EN	x				
Western Woolly Lemur	Avahi occidental	*Avahi occidentalis*	VU	x				
Bemaraha Woolly Lemur	Avahi de Cleese	*Avahi cleesei*	CR	x				
Sambirano Woolly Lemur	Avahi unicolore	*Avahi unicolor*	CR	x				
Verreaux's Sifaka	Sifaka de Verreaux	*Propithecus verreauxi*	CR	x				
Decken's Sifaka	Sifaka de Decken	*Propithecus deckenii*	CR	x				
Crowned Sifaka	Sifaka couronné	*Propithecus coronatus*	CR	x				
Coquerel's Sifaka	Sifaka de Coquerel	*Propithecus coquereli*	CR	x				
Tattersall's Sifaka	Sifaka de Tattersall	*Propithecus tattersalli*	CR	x				
Diademed Sifaka	Sifaka à diadème	*Propithecus diadema*	CR	x				
Milne-Edwards's Sifaka	Sifaka de Milne-Edwards	*Propithecus edwardsi*	EN	x				
Silky Sifaka	Sifaka soyeux	*Propithecus candidus*	CR	x				
Perrier's Sifaka	Sifaka de Perrier	*Propithecus perrieri*	CR	x				
Indri	Indri	*Indri indri*	CR	x				

AYE-AYE DAUBENTONIIDAE p. 82

			Status	Madagascar	Comoros[a]	Seychelles	Réunion	Mauritius[b]
Aye-aye	Aye-aye	*Daubentonia madagascariensis*	EN	x				

OLD WORLD MONKEYS CERCOPITHECIDAE p. 139

			Status	Madagascar	Comoros[a]	Seychelles	Réunion	Mauritius[b]
Long-tailed Macaque	Macaque crabier	*Macaca fascicularis*						i

			Status	Madagascar	Comoros[a]	Seychelles	Réunion	Mauritius[b]

HARES AND RABBITS LEPORIDAE p. 140

Common name	French	Scientific	Status	Madagascar	Comoros[a]	Seychelles	Réunion	Mauritius[b]
European Rabbit	Lapin de garenne	Oryctolagus cuniculus					i	i
Indian Hare	Lièvre à col noir	Lepus nigricollis			i	i	i	i

POUCHED RATS, CLIMBING MICE AND FAT MICE NESOMYIDAE p. 83

Common name	French	Scientific	Status	Madagascar	Comoros[a]	Seychelles	Réunion	Mauritius[b]
White-tailed Tree Rat	Antsangy à queue blanche	Brachytarsomys albicauda	LC	x				
Hairy-tailed Tree Rat	Antsangy à queue touffue	Brachytarsomys villosa	VU	x				
Robert's Forest Rat	Voalavoanala	Gymnuromys roberti	LC	x				
Northern Naked-tail Forest Mouse	Voalavo à queue nue	Voalavo gymnocaudus	LC	x				
Eastern White-tailed Mountain Mouse	Voalavo d'Antsahabe	Voalavo antsahabensis	EN	x				
Grandidier's Tufted-tail Rat	Rat-loir de Grandidier	Eliurus grandidieri	LC	x				
Rock-loving Tufted-tail Rat	Rat-loir des tsingys	Eliurus tsingimbato	NE	x				
Ellerman's Tufted-tail Rat	Rat-loir d'Ellerman	Eliurus ellermani	DD	x				
Tanala Tufted-tail Rat	Rat-loir tanala	Eliurus tanala	LC	x				
Western Tufted-tail Rat	Rat-loir de Milne-Edwards	Eliurus myoxinus	LC	x				
Lesser Tufted-tail Rat	Petit Rat-loir	Eliurus minor	LC	x				
Webb's Tufted-tail Rat	Rat-loir de Webb	Eliurus webbi	LC	x				
Petter's Tufted-tail Rat	Rat-loir de Petter	Eliurus petteri	EN	x				
Tsingy Tufted-tail Rat	Rat-loir d'Antsingy	Eliurus antsingy	DD	x				
Carleton's Tufted-tail Rat	Rat-loir de Carleton	Eliurus carletoni	LC	x				
Major's Tufted-tail Rat	Rat-loir de Major	Eliurus majori	LC	x				
White-tipped Tufted-tail Rat	Rat-loir à queue blanche	Eliurus penicillatus	EN	x				
Daniel's Tufted-tail Rat	Rat-loir de Daniel	Eliurus danieli	LC	x				
Western Big-footed Mouse	Kelibotra de Bastard	Macrotarsomys bastardi	LC	x				
Petter's Big-footed Mouse	Kelibotra de Petter	Macrotarsomys petteri	DD	x				
Long-tailed Big-footed Mouse	Kelibotra d'Ankarafantsika	Macrotarsomys ingens	EN	x				
Koopman's Mountain-dwelling Mouse	Voalavo de Koopman	Monticolomys koopmani	LC	x				
Malagasy Giant Jumping Rat	Vositse géant	Hypogeomys antimena	EN	x				
Lesser Short-tailed Rat	Petit Ramirohitra	Brachyuromys betsileoensis	LC	x				
Greater Short-tailed Rat	Grand Ramirohitra	Brachyuromys ramirohitra	LC	x				
Eastern Red Forest Rat	Nésomys roux	Nesomys rufus	LC	x				
Lowland Red Forest Rat	Nésomys d'Audebert	Nesomys audeberti	LC	x				
Tsingy Red Forest Rat	Nésomys de Lamberton	Nesomys lamberton	EN	x				

TRUE MICE AND RATS, GERBILS AND RELATIVES MURIDAE p. 140

Common name	French	Scientific	Status	Madagascar	Comoros[a]	Seychelles	Réunion	Mauritius[b]
Brown Rat	Rat brun	Rattus norvegicus		i	i	i	i	i
Roof Rat	Rat noir	Rattus rattus		i	i	i	i	i
House Mouse	Souris domestique	Mus musculus		i	i	i	i	i

SHREWS SORICIDAE p. 141

Common name	French	Scientific	Status	Madagascar	Comoros[a]	Seychelles	Réunion	Mauritius[b]
Etruscan Shrew	Pachyure étrusque	Suncus etruscus		i				
Asian House Shrew	Pachyure musquée	Suncus murinus		i	i		i	i

OLD WORLD FRUIT BATS PTEROPODIDAE p. 93 and p. 131

Common name	French	Scientific	Status	Madagascar	Comoros[a]	Seychelles	Réunion	Mauritius[b]
Madagascar Rousette	Roussette de Madagascar	Rousettus madagascariensis	VU	x				
Comoro Rousette	Roussette des Comores	Rousettus obliviosus	VU		x			
Madagascar Straw-coloured Fruit Bat	Roussette-paillée de Madagascar	Eidolon dupreanum	VU	x				
Livingstone's Flying Fox	Roussette de Livingstone	Pteropus livingstonii	CR		x			
Rodrigues Flying Fox	Roussette de Rodrigues	Pteropus rodricensis	EN					x

			Status	Madagascar	Comoros[a]	Seychelles	Réunion	Mauritius[b]
Aldabra Flying Fox	Roussette d'Aldabra	*Pteropus aldabrensis*	EN			x		
Madagascar Flying Fox	Roussette marron	*Pteropus rufus*	VU	x				
Seychelles Flying Fox	Roussette des Seychelles	*Pteropus seychellensis*	LC		x	x		
Greater Mascarene Flying Fox	Roussette des Mascareignes	*Pteropus niger*	EN				x	x

TRIDENT BATS RHINONYCTERIDAE p. 94 and p. 134

Rufous Trident Bat	Triaenops roux	*Triaenops menamena*	LC	x				
Golden Trident Bat	Triaenops de Grandidier	*Paratriaenops auritus*	VU	x				
Trouessart's Trident Bat	Triaenops de Trouessart	*Paratriaenops furcula*	LC	x				
Paulian's Trident Bat	Triaenops de Paulian	*Paratriaenops pauliani*	DD		x			

OLD WORLD LEAF-NOSED BATS HIPPOSIDERIDAE p. 95

Commerson's Leaf-nosed Bat	Phyllorhine de Commerson	*Macronycteris commersonii*	NT	x				
Madagascar Cryptic Leaf-nosed Bat	Phyllorhine cryptique	*Macronycteris cryptovalorona*	NE	x				

SHEATH-TAILED BATS EMBALLONURIDAE p. 96 and p. 134

Mauritian Tomb Bat	Taphien de Maurice	*Taphozous mauritianus*	LC	x	x	x	x	x
Rock-dwelling Sheath-tailed Bat	Emballonure des rochers	*Paremballonura tiavato*	LC	x				
Peters's Sheath-tailed Bat	Emballonure de Madagascar	*Paremballonura atrata*	LC	x				
Seychelles Sheath-tailed Bat	Emballonure des Seychelles	*Coleura seychellensis*	CR			x		
Madagascar Sheath-tailed Bat	Emballonure à ventre blanc	*Coleura kibomalandy*	DD	x				

MADAGASCAR SUCKER-FOOTED BATS MYZOPODIDAE p. 98

Schliemann's Sucker-footed Bat	Myzopode de Schliemann	*Myzopoda schliemanni*	LC	x				
Eastern Sucker-footed Bat	Myzopode de Madagascar	*Myzopoda aurita*	LC	x				

FREE-TAILED BATS MOLOSSIDAE p. 99 and p. 135

Peters's Goblin Bat	Molosse de Madagascar	*Mormopterus jugularis*	LC	x				
Réunion Goblin Bat	Molosse de La Réunion	*Mormopterus francoismoutoui*	LC				x	
Mauritian Goblin Bat	Molosse de Port-Louis	*Mormopterus acetabulosus*	EN					x
Malagasy Large-eared Free-tailed Bat	Tadaride de Madagascar	*Otomops madagascariensis*	LC	x				
Grandidier's Lesser Free-tailed Bat	Tadaride de Grandidier	*Chaerephon leucogaster*	NE	x	x			
Seychelles Free-tailed Bat	Tadaride des Seychelles	*Chaerephon pusillus*	VU			x		
Malagasy Eastern Free-tailed Bat	Tadaride d'Atsinanana	*Chaerephon atsinanana*	LC	x				
Malagasy Western Free-tailed Bat	Tadaride dimorphe	*Chaerephon jobimena*	LC	x				
Midas's Free-tailed Bat	Tadaride midas	*Mops midas*	LC	x				
Malagasy Large White-bellied Free-tailed Bat	Tadaride à giron blanc	*Mops leucostigma*	LC	x	x			
Malagasy Large Free-tailed Bat	Tadaride de Thomas	*Tadarida fulminans*	LC	x				

LONG-FINGERED BATS MINIOPTERIDAE p. 102

Aellen's Long-fingered Bat	Minioptère d'Aellen	*Miniopterus aelleni*	LC	x	x			
Griveaud's Long-fingered Bat	Minioptère de Griveaud	*Miniopterus griveaudi*	DD	x	x			
Glen's Long-fingered Bat	Minioptère de Glen	*Miniopterus gleni*	LC	x				
Short-tragus Long-fingered Bat	Minioptère à oreillons courts	*Miniopterus brachytragos*	LC	x				
Malagasy Northern Long-fingered Bat	Minioptère d'Ambohitra	*Miniopterus ambohitrensis*	LC	x				
Major's Long-fingered Bat	Minioptère de Major	*Miniopterus majori*	LC	x				
Eger's Long-fingered Bat	Minioptère d'Eger	*Miniopterus egeri*	LC	x				
Manavi Long-fingered Bat	Minioptère du Betsileo	*Miniopterus manavi*	LC	x				

	Common name	French name	Scientific name	Status	Madagascar	Comoros[a]	Seychelles	Réunion	Mauritius[b]
	Small Sister Long-fingered Bat	Minioptère soeur	Miniopterus sororculus	LC	x				
	Peterson's Long-fingered Bat	Minioptère de Peterson	Miniopterus petersoni	DD	x				
	Mahafaly Long-fingered Bat	Minioptère du Mahafaly	Miniopterus mahafaliensis	LC	x				
	Griffiths's Long-fingered Bat	Minioptère de Griffiths	Miniopterus griffithsi	DD	x				

VESPER BATS VESPERTILIONIDAE p. 106 and p. 136

	Common name	French name	Scientific name	Status	Madagascar	Comoros[a]	Seychelles	Réunion	Mauritius[b]
	Rüppell's Bat	Pipistrelle de Rüppell	Vansonia rueppellii	LC	x				
	Dusky Pipistrelle	Pipistrelle hespéride	Pipistrellus hesperidus	LC	x				
	Racey's Pipistrelle	Pipistrelle de Racey	Pipistrellus raceyi	DD	x				
	Dark Madagascar Pipistrelle	Vespère de Kirindy	Neoromicia bemainty	LC	x				
	Malagasy Serotine	Vespère de Madagascar	Laephotis matroka	LC	x				
	Isalo Serotine	Vespère de l'Isalo	Laephotis malagasyensis	VU	x				
	Roberts's Serotine	Vespère de Roberts	Laephotis robertsi	DD	x				
	Malagasy Western House Bat	Scotophile d'Andadoany	Scotophilus tandrefana	DD	x				
	Marovaza House Bat	Scotophile de Marovaza	Scotophilus marovaza	LC	x				
	Malagasy Large House Bat	Scotophile robuste	Scotophilus robustus	LC	x				
	Réunion House Bat	Scotophile de Bourbon	Scotophilus borbonicus	DD				x	
	Malagasy Mouse-eared Bat	Murin de Madagascar	Myotis goudotii	LC	x				
	Anjouan Myotis	Murin d'Anjouan	Myotis anjouanensis	DD		x			

RIGHT AND BOWHEAD WHALES BALAENIDAE p. 110

	Common name	French name	Scientific name	Status
	Southern Right Whale	Baleine australe	Eubalaena australis	LC

RORQUALS BALAENOPTERIDAE p. 110

	Common name	French name	Scientific name	Status
	Humpback Whale	Rorqual à bosse	Megaptera novaeangliae	LC
	Fin Whale	Rorqual commun	Balaenoptera physalus	VU
	Blue Whale	Rorqual bleu	Balaenoptera musculus	EN
	Sei Whale	Rorqual boréal	Balaenoptera borealis	EN
	Bryde's Whale	Rorqual d'Eden	Balaenoptera edeni	LC
	Omura's Whale	Rorqual d'Omura	Balaenoptera omurai	DD
	Common Minke Whale	Petit Rorqual	Balaenoptera acutorostrata	LC
	Antarctic Minke Whale	Rorqual antarctique	Balaenoptera bonaerensis	NT

SPERM WHALE PHYSETERIDAE p. 113

	Common name	French name	Scientific name	Status
	Sperm Whale	Grand Cachalot	Physeter macrocephalus	VU

PYGMY AND DWARF SPERM WHALES KOGIIDAE p. 114

	Common name	French name	Scientific name	Status
	Pygmy Sperm Whale	Cachalot pygmée	Kogia breviceps	LC
	Dwarf Sperm Whale	Cachalot nain	Kogia sima	LC

BEAKED WHALES ZIPHIIDAE p. 115

	Common name	French name	Scientific name	Status
	Cuvier's Beaked Whale	Baleine-à-bec de Cuvier	Ziphius cavirostris	LC
	Longman's Beaked Whale	Baleine-à-bec de Longman	Indopacetus pacificus	DD
	True's Beaked Whale	Baleine-à-bec de True	Mesoplodon mirus	LC
	Gray's Beaked Whale	Baleine-à-bec de Gray	Mesoplodon grayi	DD
	Blainville's Beaked Whale	Baleine-à-bec de Blainville	Mesoplodon densirostris	DD

OCEAN DOLPHINS DELPHINIDAE p. 118

	Common name	French name	Scientific name	Status
	Killer Whale	Épaulard	Orcinus orca	DD
	Rough-toothed Dolphin	Dauphin sténo	Steno bredanensis	LC

			Status	Madagascar	Comoros[a]	Seychelles	Réunion	Mauritius[b]
Risso's Dolphin	Grampus	*Grampus griseus*	LC					
False Killer Whale	Fausse-orque	*Pseudorca crassidens*	NT					
Pygmy Killer Whale	Orque pygmée	*Feresa attenuata*	LC					
Melon-headed Whale	Péponocéphale	*Peponocephala electra*	LC					
Long-finned Pilot Whale	Globicéphale noir	*Globicephala melas*	LC					
Short-finned Pilot Whale	Globicéphale tropical	*Globicephala macrorhynchus*	LC					
Indian Ocean Humpback Dolphin	Dauphin de Chine	*Sousa plumbea*	EN					
Common Bottlenose Dolphin	Grand Dauphin	*Tursiops truncatus*	LC					
Indo-Pacific Bottlenose Dolphin	Dauphin indien	*Tursiops aduncus*	NT					
Pantropical Spotted Dolphin	Dauphin bridé	*Stenella attenuata*	LC					
Striped Dolphin	Dauphin bleu et blanc	*Stenella coeruleoalba*	LC					
Spinner Dolphin	Dauphin à long bec	*Stenella longirostris*	LC					
Common Dolphin	Dauphin du Cap	*Delphinus delphis*	LC					
Fraser's Dolphin	Dauphin de Fraser	*Lagenodelphis hosei*	LC					

DEER CERVIDAE p. 142

			Status	Madagascar	Comoros[a]	Seychelles	Réunion	Mauritius[b]
Javan Deer	Cerf de Timor	*Rusa timorensis*						i

PIGS SUIDAE p. 142

			Status	Madagascar	Comoros[a]	Seychelles	Réunion	Mauritius[b]
Bushpig	Potamochère du Cap	*Potamochoerus larvatus*		i				

CIVETS, GENETS AND OYANS VIVERRIDAE p. 143

			Status	Madagascar	Comoros[a]	Seychelles	Réunion	Mauritius[b]
Small Indian Civet	Civette indienne	*Viverricula indica*		i				

MONGOOSES HERPESTIDAE p. 143

			Status	Madagascar	Comoros[a]	Seychelles	Réunion	Mauritius[b]
Small Indian Mongoose	Mangouste tachetée	*Urva auropunctata*		i				i

MADAGASCAR CARNIVORES EUPLERIDAE p. 125

			Status	Madagascar	Comoros[a]	Seychelles	Réunion	Mauritius[b]
Fosa	Fossa de Madagascar	*Cryptoprocta ferox*	VU	x				
Spotted Fanaloka	Fossane	*Fossa fossana*	VU	x				
Falanouc	Euplère de Goudot	*Eupleres goudotii*	VU	x				
Ring-tailed Vontsira	Galidie à queue annelée	*Galidia elegans*	LC	x				
Broad-striped Vontsira	Galidie à bandes larges	*Galidictis fasciata*	VU	x				
Brown-tailed Vontsira	Galidie unicolore	*Salanoia concolor*	VU	x				
Bokyboky	Galidie à dix raies	*Mungotictis decemlineata*	EN	x				

Index